THIRTEEN
MOST PLEASANT
AND DELECTABLE
QUESTIONS
OF LOVE

THIRTEEN MOST PLEASANT AND DELECTABLE QUESTIONS OF LOVE

Entitled

A DISPORT OF DIVERSE NOBLE PERSONAGES

Written in Italian by

GIOVANNI BOCCACCIO
*Florentine and Poet Laureate
in his Book*

FILOCOLO

First Turned into English by H.G. in 1566
and now refashioned
and illustrated by

HARRY CARTER

Clarkson N. Potter, Inc.   *Publisher, New York*

DISTRIBUTED BY CROWN PUBLISHERS, INC.

CONTENTS

INTRODUCTION

GIOVANNI BOCCACCIO WAS BORN IN 1313, PERHAPS IN PARIS, AND DIED IN 1375 in Certaldo, a small windy hilltop town overlooking the main road that turns south from Florence. The identity of his mother is uncertain, as is the place of his birth. There is, however, good reason to believe that she was French, for Giovanni's earliest memories are of that language. His father, an enterprising moneylender from Florence attracted by tales of quick fortune and the easy life of Paris, had made his way there sometime around 1312. The times were in ferment, society was fluid, and money for high interest was in good demand. He had no reason to be disappointed in his move.

The young man found the city quite to his taste, particularly in matters of love. Established and soon well connected, he lived there pleasantly for several years, producing, if not a great fortune, an acknowledged bastard son who would in time bring honor to the family name and certain immortality to his own.

At about the age of nine Giovanni first comes to public notice, officially recorded as living with his father who has now returned to Florence and is respectably married, although not to the boy's mother. Her role fulfilled, she vanishes namelessly into history and is replaced by an unloving stepmother. According to the few autobiographical notes left by Boccaccio, these were not happy years for him. But, in 1327, the quality of his life greatly improved when his father, sent as the representative of the Bardi banking house to the Court of Naples, determined that, of his family, Giovanni alone would accompany him.

Because of his father's influential banking position and his easy access to court life, Giovanni was allowed to grow into young manhood surrounded by companions from a privileged world, and little in this city of pleasure was denied him. The study of canon law, his father's choice of career for him, fell victim to the good life. Attracted to the literary scene, and with pretensions to poetry, he turned away from a professional future and, not unexpectedly, became a discerning observer of the life and times. It was indeed the best of times for him and he spent it well, storing in the backrooms of memory much of the material that later would find its way into the exuberant tales of his greatest masterpiece, the *Decameron.*

The reigning dynasty of the kingdom of Naples was Provençal in origin. Robert the king was the third of his family in direct succession to rule over these pleasure-loving, half-pagan people. Benevolent, splendid, and brilliant, he attracted to his court some of the greatest names of the age. Artists, poets, and men of great learning flocked to Naples to freely circulate and contribute to the intellectual transformation that was taking place. Young Boccaccio was not untouched by this new independence of scholarly inquiry.

Charles of Anjou, Robert's grandfather, had brought to his new kingdom for the amusement of his court, troubadours with their songs, *jeux partis,* and, of course, the justly celebrated "courts of love." These lively diversions, still performed in Robert's time, left deep impressions on the mind of Giovanni. His response was natural and romantic. He was twenty-two years old and a poet. In love with love, he had already experienced erotic dreams in which *twice* the same beauty appeared and promised him "she who would be the real tyrant of his heart." Fulfillment of this promise was awaited eagerly, and because he believed in it, that day was not to be long delayed.

Giovanni and other young men of the town were accustomed to idling about the steps of the church of San Lorenzo, to stare in amusement at the fashionable world of Naples as it engaged in the time-honored, ceremonious *passegiata*. And there, on Holy Saturday in 1336 Giovanni, leaning against a column of the church, caught his first sudden glimpse of the face from his recurrent dream. Its owner returned his gaze; their eyes met briefly as she passed from the church to be quickly lost in the large crowd that filled the square.

Here, he tells us, was the very woman he had been promised. He loved her instantly, and without further ceremony he set about to find and commit himself to her. This was to be no spiritual union, such as satisfied Dante with his Beatrice, nor was it to be the idealized and romantic love of Petrarch for Laura. Boccaccio's desires were of the flesh and he pursued them with the single intention of consummation.

In his heart and books he called the young woman Fiammetta. The name suited her well for she was to consume him with a more fierce flame than he could at that time ever imagine.

Fiammetta was in truth the natural daughter of King Robert of Naples, the careless indiscretion of a fleeting court affair. It was an impressive connection and, although never officially acknowledged, it was a poorly kept secret that gave her certain undefined but privileged prerogatives. Raised in a convent away from the influence of the court, she had only recently made her presentation. Her name was Maria d'Aquino. Imperious and passionate, she was at the time of their meeting already married. An inconvenience perhaps, but it seemed not to have disturbed Giovanni greatly. Nor did it place him in much hazard for the moral climate of the time was openly licentious. Indeed, fidelity to one's lover frequently held precedence over the legality and rights of the marriage bed. With discretion, arrangements could be made, for this was expected of great personages.

When the strictures and tedium of an inconvenient marriage became too much for her, Maria's custom was to repair to the convent of her earlier education and seek further spiritual instruction. It was to the Convent of Sant' Arcangelo à Baiano that she would make her retreat, and it was here that Boccaccio finally met her. He at once lay siege to her heart and daily awaited the promise of her capitulation. Taking his measure with a cool eye, Fiammetta put him on leash until she could best decide how to deal with her new importunate and interesting suitor. The conquest took longer than Boccaccio anticipated—one hundred and fifty-nine days, according to his own confession. But the time was not wasted for, as we now know, Fiammetta, with an experience beyond her years, directed his energies into a time-consuming literary activity.

At first there were charming afternoon visits in the cloisters of the convent. Fiammetta with her circle of friends that now included Giovanni would linger and gossip on matters of love. Stories were related by one or another, more often than not to the twang of some lute, and then put to the question. Ballads, brought south by the Angevin troubadours of her great-grandfather's day, most certainly were among those recited or sung. We do know for sure that these included the epic *Floire et Blancheflor*, for Boccaccio himself tells us so. Fiammetta, particularly taken by this story of constant love, in his words, *"begs her poet Giovanni to preserve its memory by writing a little book in the vulgar tongue that will tell the entire history of these two, to the very end."*

And so we have the *Filocolo*, perhaps the first novel of modern

Europe. In it, Boccaccio recasts the story of Florio and Biancofiore, using it as a device to further his own suit and give verbal expression to his passion for Fiammetta. Through allusion and allegory he reveals much autobiographical information on how the affair went; its promise, its joys and pains, final betrayal and end. It is truly a labor of love. No claim to originality is made. With the simple allurement of Fiammetta in mind, Boccaccio collected all sorts of episodes and adventures, taking in haste, and without discernment, from other authors and other ages. Sometimes he copied French poems, plundering at the same time almost word for word from the antique Romans. Ovid is well mined, particularly his *Metamorphoses,* which is paraphrased throughout much of the *Filocolo.*

Boccaccio was twenty-three years old when he began the *Filocolo,* his first sustained effort in writing. In the confusion and disorder of the material, his youthful inexperience is clearly exposed, but the promise of his genius and the seeds of his future masterpiece the *Decameron* are also well indicated. The *Filocolo* is a rough diamond that is now by common consent considered unreadable. Ponderously long, it is filled with infinite digressions in which both story and the reader soon become lost. The *Filocolo* was first published in the Italian language in Venice in 1412. It has never been translated in its entirety into English. However, in the sixteenth century the *Thirteen Questions of Love* was extracted from the main body of the work and turned into English by a certain H. G. According to Edward Hutton, an acknowledged English authority on matters of Boccaccio, the identity of H. G. would seem to be either Henry Grantham or Humphrey Gifford, with the evidence weighing heavily in favor of the latter. In 1566, when seven of the tales were first published in London, Gifford was an undergraduate at

Oxford, and according to Hutton, who takes exception to the awkward translation, there is a certain resemblance in style to a later acknowledged work of the same author. Grantham, on the other hand, was a well-known and successful teacher of Italian, and such a translation would not have been worthy of him.

A second edition that included all thirteen stories translated by H. G. was published in 1571. Only one copy of this book is known to have survived, and it is now in the Bodleian Library. Evidently this was a popular book, for in 1587 a third and more complete edition was published. Three copies of this edition are known to exist. One is in the Bodleian Library, another is in the British Museum, and the third is in the Huntington Library in Pasadena, California. It is from a photographed copy of the edition belonging to the British Museum that a small 1927 edition was published by Peter Davies in London, with an introduction by Edward Hutton, and with spellings, punctuation, and structure, including errors of translation and printing, left exactly as in the 1587 original. This present version is a reworking of the 1927 Peter Davies edition.

If there was little originality in the content of this work, the style in which Boccaccio chose to express himself is another matter. John Dryden, in his essay, *Preface to Fables, Ancient and Modern*, had this to say about the writer:

He and Chaucer among other things had this in common that they refined their mother tongue; but with this difference, that Dante had begun to file *their* language, at least in verse, before the time of Boccaccio who likewise received no little help from his master Petrarch. But the reformation of their prose was wholly owing to Boccaccio himself, who is yet the standard of purity in the Italian tongue tho' many of his phrases are become obsolete, as in the process of time it must needs happen.

To be contemporary was the important factor. And herein is seen the influence of Fiammetta. For Boccaccio the center of things was no longer to be found either in the ancient or in the next world but in the actuality of the present. In Naples, intellectual activity, emerging from the Middle Ages, was shifting away from the abstruse scholasticism that revolved on theology. The immediate problems of public and private conduct were beginning to occupy the interest of young scholars. And by this redirection, from the promise of eternity to the reality of the moment, intellectual curiosity became the movement of worldliness. Boccaccio with his wit and urbanity was a pivotal figure in this change. He opened up new fields of expression, and it was most particularly in that of the pastoral epic that he gained his own literary immortality.

Latin authors, with their concern for man and man's destiny, were the source, along with the Greeks (from whom the Latin authors had in large part derived their form and matter), that set Boccaccio on the path of humanism. Virgil, who is alluded to early in the *Thirteen Questions* as "the poet called Maro," was the primer of Boccaccio's youth, and his influence on Boccaccio's writing was enduring. Throughout these tales from the *Filocolo*, the shifting emphasis between Christian faith and pagan thought suggests Boccaccio's dependence upon the classic Romans. The followers of Filocolo and Fiammetta constantly evoke the pagan gods in recounting their various chronicles; and references to classical *personae* are interwoven throughout the narrative, usually for the purpose of pointing up a moral comparison.

To please Maria, Boccaccio began the *Filocolo* not long after their first meeting in 1336. By early autumn of that year they had become lovers. The intensity of Giovanni's feeling for Maria was not returned, and much of the pain he suffered by this inequality in their relationship found its way into the *Thirteen Questions of Love*. In 1337, after completing Book Three, Boccaccio broke off the *Filocolo*. He had good reason to suspect Maria of deception; as a result his interest in the book waned and he abandoned it to embark on other writings. Excuses and separations decreed by Maria kept Giovanni in a continual state of despair throughout 1338, and by the new year the tempestuous affair was ended. It was only after Boccaccio had indeed lost Maria to another lover that he again picked up and continued the *Filocolo*. And it is in the Fourth Book, where he starts anew, that Boccaccio places this excerpt with all its unmistakable personal references, calling it *Questioni D'Amore*, known to us as the *Thirteen Questions of Love*.

The Second, Fifth, Seventh, and Eighth Questions in particular seem to point to the shipwreck of his affair. Each is directly involved in a condition that Boccaccio must have faced in the development and decline of his own relationship with Fiammetta. The Eighth Question, proposed by the young gentlewoman named Paola, presents a situation identical to that of Fiammetta in regard to Giovanni. *Of two women equally liked, whom ought a young man to prefer: The one who is inferior to him in birth and parentage and riches; or she who is superior to him in all these things?* Boccaccio, with Maria unquestionably in mind, has Fiammetta answer this question unequivocally saying that a young man should prefer without hesitation the one who is superior in birth and condition.

In the Seventh Question asked by Galeone, who in these tales is, of course, Boccaccio himself, he has Fiammetta say:

It is no part of humility for a man to take that which belongs to another, but rather an arrogance and an unfitting presumption.

Boccaccio forgot, perhaps, that he himself had first stolen Maria's favors from her husband, and his irony, intended as a rebuke to the wanton girl for her betrayal of his love, is wasted. Throughout the *Thirteen Questions of Love*, Boccaccio conceals, as he would the secret message of an acrostic poem, these lightly veiled reproaches meant for Fiammetta's eyes alone. But with little effect. They made no impression on the fickle lady and the intimacy was never resumed. For his part, the love he bore the faithless Fiammetta never diminished, and even after her death of the plague in 1348, he continued to speak and write of her with deep emotion.

Boccaccio's *Thirteen Questions of Love* with its charmingly archaic language as translated by H.G. in his final version of 1587, though readable, is now understood only with great difficulty. With the passage of time, a natural evolution of word meanings and literary style has obscured and made uncertain in part the sense of this Elizabethan work.

It is not the intention of the present rendering to provide completely contemporary dress for the original translation. Renaissance language is retained wherever possible, not so much to satisfy the demands of objective correctness as to provide a more highly subjective feeling for the spirit of the period. However, the beauty of language is not only in the word but in its meaning as well. The purist who claims a certain veneration due to an old language forgets that there is little pleasure and less profit in understanding a meaning imperfectly; and where it is no longer understood at all, its beauty must be assumed to have also become impaired.

Altogether full of guileless charm and innocent conceits, this excerpt from the story of Filocolo was clearly intended by Boccaccio as a divertissement. And in one sense that is what has been attempted in this reworking of the earlier writing. Nothing from the original translation has been omitted. Words have been changed or added, and structure rearranged only when cadence and flow of language required it. The vocabulary of H.G. has been enlarged at times to avoid the monotony of repetitions that frequently mar the style of his translation.

The author of this new version is also the designer of its special contents. In a period of declining manners, a reworking of the tales, with illustrations in the light and flavor of that time, seemed even more pointed and worth presenting. Courtesy and good manners are the easing element of good relations between civilized men and women. Boccaccio understood this. To feel the authentic voice of the genuine man behind these stories the artist has tried to suggest rather than record or imitate exactly the woodcut illustrations of the period when Giovanni Boccaccio's tales were first presented in printed form, more than 130 years after they were written. Architectural detail in the drawings, a tapestried fabric, the features, and more importantly, the attitudes of the men and women are all of that later period in which ceremony and social behavior had become more formally crystallized. Anachronistic, perhaps, but more flamboyant and colorful than those of the mid-fourteenth century which were plain and severe and ecclesiastic in style. This may be claimed as an artist's prerogative, and the indulgence of the critic is requested.

Coming to the end of these comments on (and apologies for) this version of the *Thirteen Questions of Love*, we leave the tales now to the reader, each of whom must draw from them in his own fashion what he may. The moral and ethical lessons are explicit, and as H.G. says so elegantly in his dedication to the Right Worshipful Mr. William Rice, Esquire: "Never doubting but as the reading of it shall bring pleasure and delight, with all due consideration, so the substance being there shall give sundry profitable lessons well worth the following of it."

Florio, the Pilgrim of Love, has set sail, and under a lowering sky approaches the south coast of Italy.

H.C.

THIRTEEN
MOST PLEASANT
AND DELECTABLE
QUESTIONS
OF LOVE

To

the Right Worshipful

M. William Rice, Esquire

H.G.

Wishes a Happy Long Life,

with increase

of Much Honor

IN HOW MUCH THE THANKFUL SORT ARE DESIROUS (AS REASON WILLS, AND experience daily teaches) to gratify such their dear friends, as to whom for various good turns and received benefits they are not a little beholden, the sundry dealing of thousands daily in use and apparent to the world, to the great praise and commendation both of one and the other, gives sufficient testimony.

So that, taking occasion thereby to shew the good will I have, to pay in part the debt many years due for your bounty towards me (the least spark of which I am unable to satisfy), I do now for your account give you, and to such others as shall vouchsafe thereof, the protection of this Italian Disport which I have turned out of his native attire into our English habit, to the end that the same may march abroad under your charge and be no less familiar to you in its recounting than it is either to the Italian or the French. Not doubting but as the reading of it shall bring pleasure and delight, so will the substance being there all duly considered give sundry profitable lessons well worth the following of it.

And because the name of its author, of no small credit with the learned for the many and various well-written works attached to it, is of itself sufficient to carry greater commendation than my pen is able to set down, I leave instead this effort, with the hope that my lack may not be the occasion to the withholding of his due praise.

And until Fortune (that only hope of the unhappy) shall make me better able, I shall desire you thankfully to accept this as a token and pledge of the goodwill I have to perform, which, for whatever purpose, my ability is unable to stretch.

Thus taking my leave, I betake you to the tuition of almighty God, who in his pleasure will preserve you in health, and after this life make you possessor of those joys of which we all hope to be partakers.

H.G. 6. March. 1566

THE BOOK TO THE READER

Look ere thou leap, judge not by view of face
Lest haste make waste in misjudging the case:
For I teach not to Love, not yet his Lore,
Nor with what salve is cured such a sore.
But I, concerned with cares that thereby haps
The bliss with joys, the storms with thunderclaps,
The courtesies where most his force is shewed
The choice of best be it good or lewd,
Compare them so, as doomed is the doubt
Thereof, and is the truth well sifted out:
The which to read such pleasure thou shall find
As may content a well-disposed mind.

. . . was set upon suddenly and without mercy by the fierce winds. Throughout the obscure and dark night the small vessel that held their security was driven into great dangers.

FLORIO, SO-CALLED FILOCOLO,[1] IN COMPANY WITH THE DUKE OF Montorio, Ascaleon, Menedon, and Massalino, sailing in search of his beloved friend Biancofiore, was set upon suddenly and without mercy by the fierce winds. Throughout the obscure and dark night the small vessel that held their security was driven into great dangers. But these perils being once passed without too desperate an injury to their ship, the voyagers at long length found themselves cast into the port of ancient Parthenope.[2]

There the storm-weary mariners found safe haven, and taking comfort in their free deliverance without yet knowing into what coast Fortune had forced them, they yielded up thanks to their gods and set about to wait out the new day. With the appearance of the first light the place of their refuge was seen to be as some had so described. Happy in this discovery, they made their way to the shore, seeming as if to come forth newly risen again out of their sepulchres rather than from ship disembarked. Looking back toward the wayward waters as they recounted to each other adventures of the spent night, they scarcely yet believed themselves secured. With one voice they praised the gods for guiding them safe out of so crooked a course and received comfort in return for their humbly offered sacrifices.

The company was received most honorably into the city by a friend of Ascaleon and there set about at once to have their ship newly fitted and decked of mast and sail, with better rudder than the one so recently lost. In this manner the mariners passed the time in Parthenope, tarrying beyond their expectation and attending the continuance of their voyage now so long delayed. Filocolo would many times have taken up his quest by land, but in this was discouraged each time by the caution of Ascaleon. And so it happened that he and his companions, impatiently waiting out a more favorable hour, remained in the aforesaid place seeing Phebea[3] five times round and as many times hornèd, before Notus saw fit to abandon his violent forces.

Almost never during this long delay did they find occasion to be light in heart. Filocolo, growing weary of the tedium and desiring only to undertake his deferred journey, one day called his companions to him and said:

"Let us go take the pleasant air, and in so passing the time upon the salt seashore proceed to reckon and provide for our future voyage."

Thus, he set forth leaning arm in arm with the Duke Parmenio, the others closely following in their lead. Filocolo, guiding them in the direction of a certain place where rest the ashes of the renowned poet called Maro,[4] kept a pleasant pace, discoursing all the while on sundry matters with his companions.

They walked for some time and were not gone so far from the city, when approaching the confines of a great garden they heard coming from therein merry sounds of the joyous feasting and pleasantries of gentlemen, dames, and young damsels. The air resounded with the noise of various instruments, as though it were the music of angelic voices. With sweet delight it entered into the hearts of all upon whose ears it fell. The sweetness of the sound did so please Filocolo that Ascaleon, restraining all talk, tarried them a while to the end that his friend's former melancholy might little by little depart away.

And while Fortune held them thus intently listening without the garden wall, there came from the enclosure a young gentleman of sumptuous attire named Galeone.[5] Espying them so assembled, and observing at once by their appearance and deportment that they were noble gentlemen he turned back and beckoned his companions, saying: "Come, let us welcome certain young men seeming to be persons of great rank who, hesitant of intruding without our bidding, stand outside these walls and give ear to our diversions."

In great curiosity they left off their pleasures and went from the garden to greet the strangers. Approaching Filocolo, whom they recognized as leader above all the others, they addressed themselves to him with a respect that only propriety could most conveniently devise to welcome such guests. They implored him to do them honor by joining in their disport, insisting all the while, through many requests, that he in no way deny them this courtesy. They described how great their pleasure would be were he and his company to join them in their garden, where others, impatient to pay their own gentle compliments, awaited their acceptance.

These sweet entreaties so pierced the heart of Filocolo (and no less the hearts of his companions) that he answered in this manner: "Friends, such a feast was truly neither sought after nor from it now so easily fled. Storm-weary shipmates cast by Providence into your port, we are yet held therein by the still angry seas. We happened by these sea banks to the end that drowsy thoughts sprung from our idleness might sooner be dispelled in the recitation of our adversities. How Fortune enticed us thus in giving ear to your gathering I understand not, unless, as we may choose to think, She in whom I know infinite mercies, desirous of removing all pensiveness from us has made us this offering. We will indeed satisfy your desire, though in doing so we become by chance lacking in the courtesies toward others that very well should proceed from ourselves."

And so, talking together cheerfully they entered the garden where the others waited to receive and bid them welcome.

Filocolo and his friends then feasted with them for some time, enjoying all the while the many other diversions that were offered. In good manners, thinking the time was now come to make their departure, Filocolo, rising to take leave, gave thanks to them all for the honor they so generously had bestowed upon his company. But with these farewells a hush fell upon the assembly until a certain lady, perhaps more illustrious than the rest and endowed with marvelous beauty and virtue, came forward to the place wherein he stood. She spoke her disappointment, and with serious expression said to him in part: "Most noble sir, in your courtesy you have this morning shown no small pleasure to these young gentlemen, and for this they shall in all ways be beholden to you. That is to say, they are obliged in that you have granted them honor in attending our little feast. May it please you now to refuse not these other most excellent dames such a favor as I secondarily entreat."

In a sweet voice Filocolo answered: "Gentle Lady, nothing may be justly denied you. Command me therefore, for my companions and I are prisoners all to your will."

The lady replied: "For so much as your coming with so noble and goodly a company has increased our festivities, I shall desire that you not lessen the same by this premature departure, but rather help us to spend the full day even to the last hour, to the end that we have already begun the same."

As she spoke, Filocolo gazed in transport upon her face. Her eyes, replete with burning rays, sparkled like the Morning Star. So pleasant and fair was she that he thought never to have seen (his Biancofiore excepted) such a creature. Made captive by her demand, he answered: "I shall willingly dispose myself to your desire rather than my own. For whatever reason so long as it shall please you, that long will I abide with you, as will my companions likewise do."

Thanking him in a most gracious a manner for this pledge, the lady returned to her place, and together with the others engaged once more in their graceful pursuits.

And so staying, Filocolo found himself entered with great familiarity in a conversation with the young gentleman named Galeone. Adorned with good qualities and of singular eloquence, he showed particular friendliness toward Filocolo. They conversed together on sundry philosophic matters, and Filocolo, looking about the happy company, remarked on its uncommon unity, saying to him as he spoke of it: "O how much more than any other are you beholden to the immortal gods! Certainly, it must be they alone who preserve you with one will in the midst of this merrymaking!"

"Indeed, we do acknowledge we are greatly in their debt," answered Galeone, "but what particular occasion is it that moves you to say this?"

Filocolo answered him: "Truly no other cause but that I see you all assembled in one good will."

"O," said Galeone, "marvel not on that account," and turning to the gathering of young ladies, he pointed: "In whom all excellence does rest, it is she, who so recently made of you her gracious captive, who both attracts and holds us herein."

"Then," said Filocolo, "this lady of such surpassing worthiness, tell me who she is. If my demand be not unlawful, disclose her name and what and whence is she? So exceeding fair by sight, of what parentage is she descended?"

"In no way may your request be unjust, for there is no one

speaking of her in public who does not swear to publish at once the renown of so worthy a lady, and so I shall indeed satisfy your curiosity. Among us she is called Fiammetta. Howbeit to the greater part of the people she is known by name of Her, through whom was contained the wound that the prevarication of the first mother opened. She is daughter to the most high Prince under whose sceptre these countries are peacefully governed. And she is also Lady to us all. Briefly, there is no virtue that ought to be in a noble heart that is not already found in hers, as I think you in tarrying here this day with us shall soon have experience thereof."

"Her appearance conceals nothing of all you say," said Filocolo. "The gods have guided her to a perfection that is merited by her singular gifts. For assuredly, I believe both that and much more than you have affirmed. Now to these other noble ladies, tell me if you will, who are they?"

"Of these gentlewomen," said Galeone, "some are presently of Parthenope, while others are from places elsewhere, come hither into her company as did yourselves."

Conversing thus a good pace, Galeone, thinking of other things, said: "O, my gentle friend, if it might not displease you it would content me to know further of your own condition and rank than is immediately apparent in your outward appearance. For, by so knowing, we may then do you the honor you must worthily merit. It sometimes happens that want of knowledge brings lack of duty in not paying due respect to those that honor others."

Filocolo answered him: "No lack of reverence could in any way occur on your behalf. To the contrary, you have so far exceeded in this that the bound and limits thereof have well been passed. But so wishing to know further of my condition, what it is proper to reveal, I shall tell you. I am a poor Pilgrim of Love, and go, as you see, seeking a lady of mine lost to me through the cunning and deceit of my own parents. And these gentlemen whom you see in my company, of their courtesy, keep by me in my pilgrimage. By name I am called Filocolo, by birth a Spaniard, and in seeking out the island of Sicilia was driven by tempest and winds into your port."

Florio knew not to talk so indiscreetly that the young gentleman would discover more of his state than he willingly desired that he should. And Galeone, having compassion for his misfortunes, comforted him in sundry ways. He foretold in words filled with promise a more fortunate life for his friend from that time on.

And to extend further his honor among the others, Galeone willed that deference be paid him not as a pilgrim or bidden guest but rather as the chief and principal patron of the feast. In agreement, the Lady commanded especially that this should be considered so, for she understood well from the report of Galeone the state of Filocolo's condition, and dearly esteemed the grievousness of the situation.

Apollo was now with his lighted chariot mounted to the meridian circle. And scarcely did he behold with so equally a positioned eye the new-appareled earth, than the dames, damsels, and young gentlemen, assembled so together in order to flee the noisome heat offending their delicate bodies, began soon to seek out shadier and more delightful quarters of the garden. Setting their feast aside for the moment, they separated into several companies for the undertaking of other gentle entertainments.

Accompanied by four others, Fiammetta turned to Filocolo and took him by the hand, saying: "Sir, the heat does constrain us to seek out some fresher air. Let us go, therefore, to yonder meadow that lies beyond us, and with sundry discourses try to forget the heat of day."

Filocolo, praising the lady's suggestion, followed in her direction with his companions. And Galeone, as well, with two others went to the appointed meadow, so fair of grass and flowers that the air was filled with a savory of sweetest scents. Around this verdant place grew an abundance of young trees, pleasing and thick with leaves, by which the meadow was well defended from the parching beams of the great sun. And there, also in its midst, was a fountain pure and clear like crystal, near which they did settle and arrange themselves.

While some did gaze into the waters and others plaited flowers, they began to talk on various matters. But, because at times, unthinking, one did interrupt another's tale, the fair lady spoke and said to them all:

"To the end that our discourse may proceed in a more orderly manner and continue until the fresh, cool hours for which we await our further feasting, let us ordain, among ourselves, one in particular to be our king. And then to him, each of us shall propound a Question of Love so that in return we may receive an apt and suitable resolution to such a question submitted. Truly, as I think, we shall no sooner have made an end to our questions but that the heat shall have passed without our knowing, and the time will have been well spent to our profit and delight."

Greatly pleased by this device the company immediately looked among themselves for so favored a leader. With one voice they chose Ascaleon as their king, for certainly, he was more grown in years than any of the rest and the very one as would constitute and yield true answers to all their demands. But to such a choosing Ascaleon answered that he must altogether be insufficient for so great an office, being more in the service of Mars than of Venus. Yet he did beseech them to leave him the choice of such a one. Knowing so well beforehand the qualities of each, and since he would not take the dignity upon himself, they did wholly consent that the election should freely be remitted to him.

Rising from his seat, Ascaleon went to a green laurel whose shade overspread the freshet of water and gathered from it certain twigs and branches of leaves. From them he devised a rich coronet and brought it into the presence of them all, speaking in this manner as he did so: "From the time that I in my most youthful years did begin to have understanding, I swear by those gods in whom I do worship that I do not remember having seen or heard named a woman of like worthiness to Fiammetta, of whom love holds us all inflamed here in her presence, and by whom we have this day been honored in such sort as we ought never to forget the same. Because she (as without doubt I know) is plentifully endowed with every grace, adorned both with beauty and virtue and endowed further with a flowing eloquence, I therefore make choice of her to be our queen. For assuredly, it is convenient that the imperial crown be bestowed upon her magnificence. Being descended from lineage royal, to whom the secret ways of Love are (as they all are) open, it shall be an easy matter for her to content us in our questions of the same."

And this being said, he humbly kneeled before this noble lady, offering the crown and saying:

"Most courteous Lady, vouchsafe to deck your head with this crown. For no less dearly is it esteemed, of them that are worthy

through their virtues to cover their heads with the like, than if it were gold."

To this the lady, with a blush newly painting her pale visage, replied: "Truly, you have not in due sort provided a queen for these amorous people that have more need of a most able king, for of all you who are present I am the most simple and of least virtue. Neither is there any one of you that is not more suitable to be invested of such a crown than I am. But so it thus pleases you, I cannot withstand your election. And to the end that I be not found contrary to our made promise, I will receive it and, as I hope, in addition receive from the gods the strength due to such office. Through the help of him to whom these leaves were always acceptable, I shall answer you all according to my small knowledge. Nevertheless, I devoutly entreat him that he will enter into my breast and invest my voice with the same that found him cause to deserve the valiant, vanquished Marsyas[6] to be drawn forth from the sheath of all his members.

"I by way of amusement shall give you light answers without sifting to the depth of your propounded questions, the going about in search of which might rather bring tediousness than delight to your minds."

And having so spoken, Fiammetta took with her delicate hand the offered garland, and there before them all set it upon her head. On pain of being deprived of the amorous joys, she then commanded that each one should prepare to put forth some question which might be apt and convenient to the purpose of which they did intend to treat. And such a one that should rather be an increaser of mirth, than one that, through too great a subtlety or otherwise, be a destroyer of the same.

THE FIRST QUESTION
proposed by Filocolo

(A young woman, asked to show which of two lovers she loves the more, each of whom claims to be the favored one, places her own garland on the head of one, and taking from the other the one he wears, dons it herself. To which did she show the more favor?)

Remaining thus for some time in this contention, they soon through many words found themselves at daggers drawn.

O N THE RIGHT HAND OF THE QUEEN SAT FILOCOLO, TO WHOM SHE turned and made this address: "Noble sir, you shall begin to set forth your question to the end that the rest, in the order that we are here placed after you, may with more certainty propound as well our own." To this Filocolo answered: "Most noble Lady, without any further delay I shall obey your commandment." And thus he began:

•

In the city where I was born, I do remember once, in honor of the same, there was made a bountiful and great feast at which were many gentlemen and gentlewomen. And I, that was there likewise roaming about and beholding them that were in the place, spied among the rest two young men, most gracious to behold, earnestly eyeing an exceeding fair and gentle young woman. Nor was I in any way able to distinguish which of them her beauty had most inflamed. And, as she in like sort had for some time beheld them without showing any more favor to one than to the other, they between themselves began to importune her. Among other words I understood of their talk was that each said he was her best beloved. And for proof thereof, one and the other of them, in the furtherance of his cause, cited various tokens previously shown him by the young woman.

Remaining thus for some time in this contention, they soon through many words found themselves at daggers drawn. And herein they acknowledged that they did very evil, for in thus doing, they wrought hurt and shame to themselves and displeasure to the lady. Wherefore, in equal agreement, both of them went before the mother of the maid, who was also at the feast, saying to her that, more than any other, each of them best liked her daughter above all other women in the world. Yet, in no way could they agree as to which of them was best liked in return. To the end that no greater inconvenience might spring thereof, would it please her to grant them, therefore, the favor that she command her daughter to show either by word or deed which of them she best loved?

The entreated gentlewoman, smiling, did agree to this in good-will, and calling her daughter to her, said: "My fair daughter, each of these young men prefers the love of you above the love of himself, and in this rivalry they beg which of them is best loved of thee. They seek this favor of me, that you resolve them in this matter either by sign or by word, to the end that Love, from whom all peace and goodness seeks always to spring, therefore breed not now the contrary, but content them in this; and so with seemly courtesy show toward which of them thy mind is most bent."

This pleased the young damsel right well, and gazing upon them both for a time she saw that one had upon his head a fair garland of fresh flowers, and that the other did stand without any garland at all. She that had in like manner a garland of green leaves upon her own brow took first the same from her head and set it upon him that stood before her without a garland. Then taking that which the other young man had upon his head, she thereupon set the same upon her own. And so leaving them she returned to the feast, saying that she had performed both the commandment of her mother and each their desire. The young men being thus left, returned at once to their former dispute, each one insisting that she loved him best.

He whose garland she took and set upon her head said: "Assuredly she loves me best, for what is mine pleases her. She has taken my garland, to no other end but give occasion to be beholden to me. But to thee, like some country girl she has given hers as it were, in place of her last farewell, unwilling that the love you carry for her be without requital. Therefore, she gives you lastly the very garland you have merited."

The other, replying to the contrary, answered in this manner: "Truly she loves that which is thine better than thyself, and such may be seen in her taking it from thee. And me, she assuredly loves better than that which is mine, for she has given me what was her own. It is no token of her last deserved gift, as you so affirm, but rather a beginning of amity and love. A gift makes the receiver a subject to the giver. And, because she is perhaps uncertain of me, to the end that she be more certain to have me her subject she binds me to her by gift, if by chance I were not bound to her before. But how can you think, if she at the beginning takes away from thee, she will ever vouchsafe to give thee at all?"

And thus they abode in contention a long time and, without any definition at all, in the end departed.

•

"Now I say most gracious Queen, if you should be demanded of the final sentence to such a quarrel, what would you judge?"

Somewhat smiling, the fair lady turned toward Filocolo, her eyes sparkling with an amorous light, and after a soft sigh made answer: "Most noble youth, your question is well put. And truly, as very wisely the young woman behaved herself so each of the young men right well defended his own cause. But because you require what we lastly will determine thereof, we make thus your answer.

"It seems to us, and so it ought to seem to each one that takes good heed, the woman hated neither the one nor the other. But to keep her intent covert, did two contrary acts. And as it appears, not without occasion, it was but wisely done to the end that she might more firmly secure the love of him she loved without losing the love of the other whom she hated not. But to come to our question: To which of the two was the greater devotion shown?

"We say that she loved him best, and he was chiefly in her favor, to whom she gave her garland. And this would seem our reasoning: Whatsoever man or woman that loves any person, each one is so strongly bound to the other loved, through force of the love he bears, that above all other things he desires to please the same, needing neither gifts nor devices to bind him or her in so loving. And this is most obviously shown to be so. Yet, we see that he who so loves, though he endeavor himself in various ways, is not able to make the beloved in any way benign and subject to him so that he may bring it to his pleasure and thereby, with a bolder face, demand his desire. And this, in such manner as we describe, the inflamed Dido[7] with her doings does very well show the same to us. Burning in the love of Aeneas and, as it seemed, neither with honors nor with gifts able to win him, she had not the courage to attempt the doubtful way by asking the question. And thus did the young woman seek to make him whom she loved best most beholden to her. Thus we say that he who received the gift of the garland was her best beloved."

As the queen fell silent, Filocolo then answered: "Discreet Lady, greatly is your answer to be commended. You do bring me into a great admiration of all which you have defined touching on the propounded question. Yet for all that, I would have judged rather to the contrary. For this was the custom, and generally so among lovers. That is, the desire to press upon a person's beloved some jewel or other thing to the end that they might ever glory themselves more in this than in all the raiment they had. Reminded by this token ever about them their minds were lifted in encouragement, as you well know. Paris[8] seldom if ever entered into bloody battle against the Greeks without bearing some talisman upon his person given him by his Helen, believing better to prevail therewith than if he had gone without the same. And truly, in my opinion his thought was not vain. Therefore, I should say as you have said, that the young lady did very wisely, not defining it at all as you have done, but in this manner: Knowing that she was very well loved of the two young men, and that she could love not more than one, for love is an indivisible thing, she would reward one for his love, to the end that such goodwill go not unrewarded. In requital thereof, she gave him her garland. To the other, whom she did love, she thought to give encouragement and assured hope of her love. So taking his garland and decking herself therewith, she plainly showed by this token to be beholden to him for the same. And therefore, in my judgment she loved him better from whom she took, than to whom she gave."

To this artful reasoning the queen made answer: "Your argument should have pleased us right well if you yourself in your tale had not condemned the same. Tell me how pillage and perfect love can agree together? How can you show me that we love him whom we despoil better than him to whom we give? According to the question propounded, to one is given a garland and from the other a garland is taken. He to whom she gave had nothing in return to give. And that which we see every day for example may here suffice. As is commonly said, gentlemen on whom are bestowed gifts and favors are far better loved than those that are deprived of them. And for that reason we lastly hold opinion, concluding that he is better loved to whom is given than he from whom is taken. We know very well that in these reasonings much might be objected against our definition, and much answered to the contrary reasons, but lastly such determination shall remain true.

"And because time now serves not to stay with our talk upon one matter only without settlement, we will give ear to the rest if it please you."

Filocolo replied that it pleased him right well, and that such a resolution very well sufficed his demanded question. And so he held his peace.

THE SECOND QUESTION
proposed by Longano

(Which is the more unhappy: the lady who, after having tasted of love, loses the lover who must go into exile without hope of return; or she to whom Fate has never allowed to taste with a lover the joys of love at all?)

Arising to see from whom and whence issued such sadness I looked from my chamber window and observed in one other chamber two young and tearful women.

PLACED NEXT TO FILOCOLO WAS A COURTEOUS YOUNG MAN, MOST gracious to behold, whose name was Longano. No sooner had Filocolo left off his discourse than Longano began to speak: "Most excellent Queen, so well ordered has been the first question that in my conceit mine shall bring no delight at all. Yet, to the end that I be not severed from so noble a company, forth it shall." And he continued, saying:

•

It is not many days past that I, resting alone in my chamber and wrapt in troublesome thoughts (sprung from an amorous desire which with fierce battle had assaulted my heart), did hear by chance a piteous plaint. Recognizing, by occasion thereof, the sounds as coming from women and judging them by estimation to be nearby, I intentively laid my ear to the matter. Arising to see from whom and whence issued such sadness I looked from my chamber window and observed in one other chamber two young and tearful women. Adorned with an inestimable beauty and living there together without any other company, they were sisters whom I saw making this grievous lament. Withdrawing myself into a secret place without their discovering me, I continued to observe them for some time; even so, I was not able to understand everything they uttered in their sorrow. According to that which I did comprehend, the cause of their plaints seemed to be love.

With so sweet an occasion offered (being now so close), I began to shed my own trickling tears through pity. Because they persevered in their grief for a good space, I proposed to understand more clearly the occasion of their sorrow, for in truth, I was closely acquainted with them as well as being their kinsman. And so I went to them who had no sooner caught sight of me than they modestly held back their tears and endeavored at once to do me honor.

To them I said: "Gentlewomen, trouble not yourselves and neither let my coming move you to restrain your inward grief, for your tears have been apparent to me for some time. It is needless, therefore, to hide from me, through some natural bashfulness, the cause of your plaint, for I have come here to understand the same. And be assured that you shall receive no evil requital, either in word or deed from me, but rather help and comfort in what I may be permitted."

The women greatly excused themselves, saying that they sorrowed for nothing. But yet, after I had implored them and they seeing me desirous of understanding the same, the elder thus began to say: "It is the pleasure of the gods that our secrets be revealed to thee. You therefore must understand that we above all other women have always resisted the sharp darts of Cupid, who of a long season in casting the same was never yet able to fasten any one of them in our hearts. But now, being further inflamed and more determined than ever to succeed in that childish enterprise, he has again taken his best and dearest shafts with his young arm, and with a mighty force wounded these hearts so sorely enfeebled through the sundry blows already received. As the barbs therefore pierced deep, so did they make a far greater wound than would have been, had resistance not been made to his earlier attacks. And thus for the pleasure of two most noble young gentlemen, we are become the subjects to his deity, following his purpose with more perfect faith and fervent will than any other women have done. Now has Fortune and the love of our two gentlemen left us both comfortless, as I shall presently make known to you.

"I first, before my sister here, was in love. And believing it wise to consummate my desire, did in my endeavor get the beloved young gentleman so wrought at my pleasure that I found him as greatly enamored of me as I of him. But truly now the amorous flame has not through such effort ceased, neither has the desire lessened, but each one more vehemently increased. And more than ever do I now burn in his fire. In such circumstance, holding it inwardly secret, I sought how best I might mitigate and assuage the kindled flame thereof.

"It presently happened that the hornèd moon was no sooner come to his perfect roundness than my beloved unwarily did commit a fault for which he was adjudged and exiled forever from this city. Whereupon dreading death, he departed hence without hope ever to return. And now, sorrowful above all other women and more inflamed than ever, I am left both doleful and desperate without him. Because of this I grieve, and what most increases my sorrow is to see on every side the way hard to follow him. Think therefore whether I have cause to bewail me, or no."

"And this other," I then said, "why sorrows she?"

To which she answered: "My sister is likewise enamored of another, and of him again is loved above measure. And to the end that her desires should not pass the amorous paths without tasting some part of delight, she has many times endeavored herself to bring them to effect. However, contrary to her design, jealousy has always occupied and broken the way. And because she could never attain thereunto, and neither saw how to be able to do so, she is thus distressed and through fervent love consumed. Now this you may well believe if ever you were in love. Being here alone, we then began to examine our misfortunes, and knowing the same to be far greater than those of other women, we could not withhold from tears. With weeping we did sorrow at our luckless lots, as you might well perceive."

It grieved me so greatly to hear this of them that I countered with such words as seemed most yielding for their comfort, and so departed from them.

·

"Considering in mind their griefs ever since, and sometimes bethinking which of the same should be the greater, at one time I would agree to that of the one, and at another time I would yield to that of the other. And the sundry reasons each one has to lament, as it seems to me, will not allow me to stay upon one or the other. In consequence of which I remain here in doubt.

"May it therefore please you to resolve this dilemma, and tell me which of these unfortunate lovers seemed to have sustained the greater grief."

"Dear Longano, great was the sorrow of each," answered the queen. "But considering adversity to be most grievous to her that has tasted prosperity, we esteem that she that has lost her love feels the greater grief, and is of Fortune greatliest offended. Fabritius[9] never bewept the chances of Fortune, but that Pompey did is a thing very manifest. If sweet things were not tasted, the sour should be yet unknown. Medea[10] never knew (according to her own saying) what manner a thing prosperity was while she was in love, but being forsaken of Jason, bewailed her adversity. Who will ever lament for what he has not had? One will rather desire. It is deemed, therefore, that, of the two women, one wept for grief and the other did so only in longing and regret."

"Most gracious Lady, it is hard for me to agree with what you affirm," said the young gentleman Longano. "For he that has his desire of any longed-for thing ought much more to content his mind than he that desires and cannot fulfill his desire. Further, nothing is easier to lose than what Hope promises not hereafter to yield. Such ought to create unmeasurable grief. On the contrary, not being able to bring equal wills to effect does hinder such grief. Thence lamentations take place, and thence thoughts and troubles do spring. If the wills were not equal, then strength of desire should not be found wanting. But when lovers find themselves in the presence of what they desire, and cannot attain it, then do they kindle and grieve much more than if what they would have were far from them. And what, I pray you, torments Tantalus[11] in Hell but only the apples and the water. For however much they bend and swell unto his mouth, so much more afterwards, in fleeing the same, do they increase his hunger. Truly, I believe that he who hopes for a thing possible to be had, and cannot attain it through contrary resisting impediments, feels more grief than he who bewails a thing lost and irretrievable."

Then said the queen: "Your answer would have followed very well had your claim been of an old grief. Although to that, it might also be said that it is possible through forgetting the grief, to shorten the longing for the desired things; whereas, continual impediment is seen to make attainment not possible as with those lost for whom there is no hope that we should ever have them again.

"But we do dispute which of them sorrowed more grievously when you saw them sorrowing. Following the propounded question with such reasoning, we will give judgment that she who has lost her lover without hope of having him again felt the greater grief. Putting the case that it is an easier matter to lose a thing impossible to have again, nevertheless, it must be said that who loves well forgets never. The other, on careful consideration, might hope to fulfill in some future time that which she was unable to perform heretofore. For a great lessener of grief is Hope. It had sufficient force to keep chaste and to diminish the sorrows of Penelope, waiting out her endless days."[12]

THE THIRD QUESTION
proposed by a young Gentlewoman named Cara

(To which of three
aspirants should a lady give her preference? To him who excels in valor, or
to him who is most courteous and liberal, or to him who is the wisest?)

Setting apart many seekers of such love, of which some do excel Midas in riches, some others pass Absalom in beauty, and still others in courtesy (according to the common report of all) are more splendid than any other, I have of all these chosen three, each one of whom pleases me alike.

*t*O THE RIGHT OF LONGANO SAT AN EXCELLENTLY FAIR AND VERY pleasant gentlewoman who, as she perceived that question by Fiammetta determined, began in a sweet voice to say: "Most renowned Queen, your ears grant hearing to my words. And first by those gods whom you worship, and next by the power of our pastime, I pray that you will give profitable counsel to my demand.

"I was born in this city as you know, being descended of noble parents and named with a very gracious name, although my given name (being Cara) presents me more pleasingly to the ears. And as by my face it may appear I have received from the gods and nature a singular gift of beauty, in following my proper name more than my surname, I have adorned it with an infinite pleasantness, showing myself of gentle nature to all that delight in beholding the same. For this reason, many for their own amusement have striven to catch my eye. Against all have I stood with strong resistance, holding a stable heart in opposition to their assaults. But because it seems to me unlawful that I alone should pass by the laws kept and observed by all others, that is, not to love being loved by many, I have determined to become enamored. Setting apart many seekers of such love, of which some do excel Midas in riches, some others pass Absalom in beauty, and still others in courtesy (according to the common report of all) are more splendid than any other, I have of all these chosen three, each one of whom pleases me alike.

"Of these three, the one of bodily force (as I believe) would excel the good Hector;[13] he is at every proof so vigorous and strong. The courtesy and liberality of the second is such that (as I think) his fame does sound throughout to each pole. The third is full of wisdom, so that he surpasses all other wise men beyond measure. Except for what you have heard, their qualities are various. I question which one of them to take, finding, as in the antique age, each of them to have diversely the courages of women and of yielding men like Deianira[14] and Hercules, of our Clytemnestra[15] and Aegisthus, and of Lucretia[16] and Sextus.

"Counsel me therefore, to which of these, soonest, with least blame and greatest surety, ought I to give myself?"

The pleasant queen, having heard the purpose of this gentlewoman, made answer: "There is not one of the three that does not merit the love of a fair and gracious lady. But because in this case we are not to fight against castles, or to give away the kingdom of great Alexander or the treasures of Ptolemy, we say that both you and every other woman ought rather to give her love to a wise man than to any of the rest. For love and honor are with discretion to be kept a long time, being maintained neither by force nor courtesy, but only by wisdom."

"O how different is my judgment from yours," answered the propounding gentlewoman. "To me it seems that each of the others were sooner to be taken than the wise. And here is my reason. Love (as we see) is of such nature that multiplying his force in one heart, he banishes every other thing, retaining only what is necessary for his effort, and moving it only according to his pleasure. For which purpose no prudence is able to resist but what is convenient for the heart to follow, governed as it is by love. And who doubts that Byblis[17] knew it to be evil to love her brother? Who will gainsay that it was apparent to Leander[18] that he might drown in the Hellespont in his fortunate time if he cast himself therein? And none will deny that Pasiphae[19] knew a man to be more fair than a bull. And yet they and each one, so overcome with an amorous pleasure, did reject all knowledge and follow their pleasure. Now if Love has power to take knowledge from the learned, taking away the wit from the wise leaves them with nothing. But if from the strong and courteous it shall take away the little wit they have, it shall yet increase them in their virtues. And so enamored, they shall become more than the wise. Further, Love has this property, in that it is a thing that cannot be long hid. In revealing himself he is ofttimes accustomed to bringing grievous perils. To what remedy shall the wise recourse, who has now lost his wit? He shall give none at all. But the strong who uses his force can help both himself and others in a peril. The courteous through his courtesy shall with grateful benevolence win the minds of many, whereby he and others may both be helped and attended to because of him. See now what it is to be of your judgment?"

To this the queen answered her in the following manner: "If there was such a one as you speak of, who should then be wise? No one. But if he whom you propound to be wise and enamored of you should be made a fool, he is not to be taken. The gods forbid lest that of which you speak should come to pass. And yet we will not deny that the wise know the evil and do it. But for all that, we will say that they do not thereby lose their wit. For as long as it pleases them, with the reason they have to bridle their wills, they will reduce themselves to their accustomed wit, guiding their emotions in a due and straight order. And in this manner their love shall be altogether, or at least, a long time kept secret. And that, without doubtful diligence, shall not happen to one of little wit, be he ever so strong or courteous. And yet, if perhaps it does happen that such love be discovered, a wise man with a hundred foresights shuts up the eyes and understanding of the tattlers thereof, providing a safeguard both for his own honor and for the honor of his beloved lady. And if need of safety exists, the help of the wise cannot fail. That of the strong comes less. And the friends who are gotten by liberality are accustomed in adversity to shrink away. What is she of so little discretion who has need of manifest help when brought to such a jump? Or, if her love be disclosed, seeks fame in having loved a strong or liberal man? I believe there is nonesuch. Let the wise then be soonest loved, hoping that he must be, in each cause, more profitable than any of the rest."

THE FOURTH QUESTION
proposed by Menedon

(A story in which the question must be resolved as to which of three persons, the husband, the lover, or the magician, has behaved most generously.)

In many different ways, now passing before her house, now jousting, now at the barriers, now with frequent messages sent by chance with promises of great gifts by which she might know his intent, and still with other like feats did he endeavor to purchase her love.

OBSERVING BY HER COUNTENANCE THAT THE GENTLEWOMAN named Cara seemed content, Menedon, who was seated next by her side, turned to the queen and said: "Most high and noble Queen, it is now come my turn to propound here in your presence my question. And by your leave, for whatever reason if in my talk I labor too long, yet during the same I shall pray ask the pardon of all of you as well they who stand about, for you cannot be made to understand fully what I intend to propound unless a tale (that peradventure shall not be short) do precede the same." Pausing briefly upon these words, Menedon then began his story:

•

In the country where I was born I recall a noble knight of great riches, who loved in a most loyal fashion a noble gentlewoman, born likewise there, whom he took to wife. Because of her exceeding beauty, another knight called Tarolfo became greatly enamored of her, and with so great a goodwill did he love her, too, that nothing he saw did he desire so much as she. In many different ways, now passing before her house, now jousting, now at the barriers, now with frequent messages sent by chance with promises of great gifts by which she might know his intent, and with still other like feats did he endeavor to purchase her love. All this the lady quietly endured without giving sign or good answer to the knight, saying to herself: When this knight discovers that he can have neither answer nor yet good countenance of me, perhaps he will forbear further to love me or offer me these continued allurements.

But for all this, Tarolfo continued his suit, following the precept of Ovid,[20] who said that a man must not, through the hardness of a woman, cease to persevere, because with continuance the soft water pierces the hard stone.

The lady, concerned that these things should come to the ears of her husband, and that he might come to believe the same did happen through her compliance, proposed to let him understand her situation. Being persuaded through other advisement, she thought better of this and said: "If I tell him, I might cause such a broil between them that I should never again live a carefree life; therefore, he must be shaken off by some other means."

And so she devised this cunning deceit. A message was sent to Tarolfo stating that if he loved her so well as he made show of, one thing would she require at his hands, and when that was received, she swore by her gods and by such loyalty as ought to be in a gentlewoman that she would accomplish all his desire. But, if he would not give her what she required, he should then content himself to leave off all further allurements hereafter, other than those he would be willing that she should reveal to her husband.

The gift she required was this: that in the month of January she would have in her country a very fair garden and large, replete with herbs, flowers, and blossoming trees, and fruits, as if it were in the month of May.

"The lady thought to herself, as she sent her message, here is an impossible do, and so now in this manner I will at last be rid of him. But Tarolfo, in receiving her demand, and although it seemed to him an impossible feat as well, knowing to what end she required the same, answered that he would never rest nor yet return into her presence until such time as he might give her the demanded gift.

"And so, forthwith he departed the country, carrying such suitable company as pleased him to take along. He sought first throughout all the western regions for counsel on how to attain his desire. Not finding what he was looking for, he journeyed further toward the warmer lands, and finally he came into Thessaly, sent there by a man of wisdom who knew of his purpose. Having made his abode for a number of days without finding what he sought, and being now almost desperate of his desire, it happened one morning that rising before the sun prepared to enter the dawning day he began to wander alone over the miserable plains that were now so deeply tinged with the color of Roman blood. Having coursed a long time upon the same, at the foot of a mountain he suddenly spied a man before him. Not young nor of too many years, he was bearded, small, and very spare of person. His attire showed him to be poor. In random fashion he roamed about gathering herbs, digging up with a little knife sundry roots with which he filled one of the skirts of his coat. As Tarolfo stood observing, he marveled not a little and wondered greatly if this might not instead be some other thing; but when his actions did certainly convince him that he must be a man, he drew nearer and greeted him. After asking by what name he was called and whence he came, he inquired what it was he made there at so early an hour.

To this the old man replied in friendly enough fashion: "I am of Thebes, and Theban is my name. I go up and down this open field in the shadow of this slope gathering these herbs, to the end that from the juices thereof I may make various necessary and beneficial things for different infirmities. It is in this manner that I acquire the wherewithal to live. And to come at this hour, it is necessity and not delight that constrains me. But who are you, that in countenance seems of noble station yet walks here alone in solitude?"

And Tarolfo answered him: "I am of the western extremes, perhaps very rich, yet vanquished of conceits, pricked forward to an enterprise of which I am still unable to achieve the same. And therefore, to be better able to bear my condition without hindrance, I go thus, all solitary, wandering."

In reply, Theban said: "Do you not know the quality of this place, and its significance? How does it happen that you took not your way on the other side? You might easily be rebuked by the furious spirits that abound here in the region."

Smiling, Tarolfo answered: "God can do here as elsewhere. It is He that has my life and honor in His hands. Let Him do with me according to His pleasure, for assuredly, death should be to me a rich treasure."

Then Theban said: "Tell me, what is this enterprise of yours, that not being able to perform it leaves you in so sorrowful a condition?"

And Tarolfo answered him: "It is such as seems impossible for me ever to attain, for I have not as yet found the one who can counsel me."

"Dare you utter it?" inquired Theban.

"Yea," replied Tarolfo, "but what use would it now serve?"

"By chance, nothing," said Theban, "but then again, what harm could it do?"

To this, Tarolfo replied: "Assuredly then, this I will tell you. I seek advice in how can be had in the coldest month, a garden full of flowers, fruits, and herbs as fair as if it were in the month of May. And in this, I have not yet found the one who can either help me or give me the encouragement that it is possible to be had."

When Theban heard this, he fell for a while in a deep muse without any reply, but in good time he spoke, answering with these words: "You judge, as do many others, the skill and virtue of men according to their raiment. If my goods had been such as yours, or had you perhaps found me near some rich prince instead of gathering these herbs, you would not so long have delayed the discovery of that which you seek. It is often so that the greatest treasures of science are hidden under the vilest vesture, and therefore, no one should conceal his need from one who offers counsel or help. For in revealing the same, no hurt can come of it at all. But still, what would you give to him who should effect that which you go about seeking in this manner?"

As he uttered these words, Tarolfo studied the old man's face closely; for he was not at all certain that these words were not said in mockery. It seemed beyond his belief that this creature should be capable of granting such a petition, unless he were, of course, a god. Nevertheless he returned him this reply: "In my country, I have under my rule many castles, and therein, moreover, great treasure. All this, I would share equally with the one who would do me so great a service."

"Truly," said Theban, "if you would do so much for me I should no more need to go about as I do in this manner gathering herbs."

"Assuredly," Tarolfo replied, "if you should be able to truly realize what you promise, and indeed, give it to me, you shall never need to concern nor yet to trouble yourself again in becoming rich. But how now? And when can you bring this to pass for me?"

"It will be done. Concern yourself not in what manner, but done it will be at the proper time," said Theban. "Now I shall go with you, trusting your word and the promises you have made to me. And when we arrive at that place wherein it pleases you to be, command me what you would have done, and I shall perform the same without fail."

Faced with such a fortunate circumstance, and so well content with his prospect, Tarolfo could hardly have been happier were he already holding his lady embraced in his arms.

He said to Theban: "Friend, to me it will seem a lifetime until you have performed what you have promised. Let us depart and with no further delay go where this is to be accomplished."

Casting his herbs away, Theban took up his books and other things necessary to his science and made his way with Tarolfo. And in a short time, very near to the month in which the garden had been required to be made, they arrived together in the desired city. Here, in close secrecy, they did quietly lay and await the auspicious moment.

As the month was about to be entered Tarolfo now commanded the garden to be made so that he might give the promised same to his beloved lady.

When Theban received his commandment he awaited the night, on which being once come, he could see the horns of the moon gathered into a perfect roundness and shining upon the frequented earth. Only then did he go from the city, alone, with his apparel left loose, bare-legged, and disheveled locks falling freely over his naked shoulders. The restless night passed slowly while birds, wild beasts, and men, without sound of any kind, took their rest. The unfallen leaves hung lightly without moving upon the trees, and the moist air abode in mild peace. Only the stars shone as Theban went questing over and over the ground.

When finally he came upon a place near the river's edge that pleased him to choose for his garden's prospect, he stretched forth his arms toward the stars and gestured three times. Turning toward them, he as often bathed his white locks in the running stream, and beseeched in a most high voice their help as many times again. And after setting his knees upon the hard earth, he began thus, the following incantation: "O Night, most faithful keeper of high and secret things! O Stars that together with the Moon do succeed the splendid Day! O singular Hecate![21] Become a helper in this my newly begun enterprise!

"And thou, O holy Ceres, renewer of the Earth's most ample surface! And thou who do versify either arts or herbs! And thou who bring forth from the Earth all fresh growing plants, do give me aid!

"And thou, O Air, Winds, Mountains, Rivers, and Lakes, and each god of the Woods, and of the secret Night by whose help I have heretofore made the running streams recoil upon themselves, enforcing them to return to their source, and things running to be made firm, and things firm to become running! And that which also has given power to my verses that dry up the sea so I at my pleasure might search the bottom thereof, and make the cloudiest times clear, and at my will to fill the clear Heavens with obscurity, to make the Winds subside and to turn as it seems best in my mind, breaking the hard jaws of the most fearful dragons, making also the standing Wood to move and the high Mountain to tremble, hear me!

"And thou, whose given power permits me to return their shadows to those whose bodies rise from out the Styx and give life to some that rise forth from their sepulchres! And sometimes thee, O Moon, to draw to thy perfect roundness, the attainment of which a ring of basins was wont to help make also the clear face of the Sun many times to become pale!

"Be ye all present, and with thy aid be of help to me. I have this instant the need of the sap, and juices of herbs, through which I may make in part the dry earth fastened through Autumn, and again through the withering cold Winter spoiled of his flowers, fruits, and herbs, to become flowering and like Spring before his due term."

And having thus spoken, he continued softly with many other things which he added to his prayers. And these being ended, and he silent awhile, the Stars gave not their light in vain. For more swifter than the flight of the most heroic bird, there appeared before him a chariot drawn by two dragons. Theban mounted and took the reins of the two bridled beasts in his hands, and was at once carried into the air.

Leaving Spain and all Africa, he took his journey by other regions, first seeking for the island of Crete. From there, after a short course, he sought Pelion, Othrys, and Offa. Flying across Mounts Nerium, Pachinus, Palorus, and Apennine, from each he plucked up and, with a sharp sickle, cut down such roots and herbs as best suited him, not forgetting others he had gathered before he was found by Tarolfo in Thessaly. He took stones also from upon the Caucasus and sands from the Ganges. And out of Libya, he brought lungs of venomous serpents. He searched the watery banks of Rodanus, of the Seine at Paris, of the great Po, of Arnus, of the Imperial Tiber, of Niscus, of Tana and Danuby. From each of these he gathered such herbs as seemed to him most necessary for his purpose, putting them together with the others that were gathered on the tops of the savage mountains. He also searched the islands of Lesbos and Patmos, and every other island from which he perceived any profitable thing to be had for his attempt.

So potent was the fragrance of the gathered herbs, the dragons, having only sensed the odor, cast off their hides of many years and were transformed and made young again.

Now with all these, Theban came to that place from which he had departed, the third day not yet being past. There he dismounted from his chariot, and of the green earth made two altars. On his right hand he constructed one for Hecate, and on the left, one for the running goddess. Such being done, and devout fires having been kindled upon each, he began with murmuring sounds to circle the same, his tangled locks falling in disorder over his old shoulders. From time to time he sprinkled the blazing brands with newly drawn blood. Placing some of this upon the two altars, he would occasionally soften the appointed ground of the garden with this concoction. After softening the earth three times again with fire, water, and sulphur, he set a great vessel full of blood, milk, and water upon the burning embers, which boiled for some time. To this he added the strange roots and herbs he had gathered in his fantastic journey, mingling with them, also, various seeds and flowers of other unknown plants. He added to this stones brought back from distant parts, and dew gathered the nights past, together with the flesh of infamous witches, the stones of a wolf, the hind part of a fat cinyphis, and the skin of a chillinder. Lastly, he increased the brew with the liver and whole lungs of an exceedingly old hart. And there withal a thousand other things did he mix without name, so strange that my memory cannot again tell of them.

After this, he took the dry bough of an olive tree, and with it began to mingle all these things together. In doing so, the dry bough began to wax green, and within a while, to bear leaves, and soon with this new appareling to become laden with black olives. When Theban saw this, he took the boiling liquors and began to sprinkle and water each section of the chosen soil wherein he had set slips of trees of as many varieties as could be found. The earth no sooner tasted of this liquor than Spring began, yielding up flowers and new herbs, with the dry settings becoming green and fruitful.

All this being done, Theban entered the city and returned to Tarolfo, whom he found all in a trance, so fearful was he of being scorned for remaining so long concealed. When Tarolfo was told that the thing required was now done and to his liking, he was well satisfied with the news.

It happened that on the following day a great solemnity was to take place in the city, so he went that same day into the presence of his beloved lady who had not seen him for a long time past, and he said to her: "Madame, after a long and tedious travail I have performed what you commanded of me. And when it shall please you to see it or take it, it is ready for your pleasure."

She wondered greatly on seeing him again, and the more so on hearing what he had to say. Not believing the same to be at all true, she answered him lightly in this manner: "It pleases me right well, and you shall let me see it tomorrow."

The second day was soon come, and Tarolfo went again to his lady and said: "Madame, may it please you to walk to the Garden that you required of me to have for you in this cold month of January?"

Forced in the end to see the same, she went with him as he directed, her many doubting companions in attendance. And when they all were assembled at the Garden's approach, they entered therein by a fair portal, and suddenly felt not the cold through which they had come but a sweetly changed and temperate air. The lady went about the Garden, marveling and gathering from its every corner both herbs and flowers. As she wandered, everywhere she went she saw abundance although the weather beyond was still savagely chill. So much had the goodness of the dispensed ichors wrought that the fruits which August was accustomed to bring forth hung heavily from their branches, yielding themselves to be eaten by the sundry companions that crowded in amazement about the lady. The Garden beyond doubt did seem exceeding fair and admirable in every way. Never had she seen its like, and as she in various ways knew it to be a true garden and the knight to have performed her request, she turned at last to him and said: "Without doubt, Sir Knight, you have deserved my love, and I am ready to stand by my word. But I would pray of you this favor, that it would please you to delay the moment when you will require me to your desire until that time when my husband may be gone hunting, or in some other place out of the city. To this end, you may then more safely and without suspicion take your promised pleasure."

Consenting to this, Tarolfo withdrew, leaving her to the Garden as he readily departed. For now the whole countryside was come upon the place in wonder, knowing not, except in rumor, how it had come to pass. And the lady that now possessed it sorrowfully departed the same, returning to her chamber full of wretched care and grief, reflecting in sundry ways how she might now repudiate her promise. And as she found no lawful way nor any excuse, her anxiety increased and multiplied her concern.

Observing the distracted condition of his lady, the husband began to wonder at it and to ask with great frequency the cause of her melancholy. To this she as often would answer that she ailed nothing, becoming more greatly concerned lest he discover the promise she had given Tarolfo in return for her demanded gift. In this she was fully convinced that he would account her lewd. But finally, unable to withstand the continual probings of her husband who so importunately desired to know the cause of her annoyance, she confessed to him, from beginning to end, the source of her concern.

The husband, on hearing her story and suspecting the same for a long time, yet knowing in his conceit the purity of the lady, answered in this manner: "Go and covertly keep thy oath, and liberally perform for Tarolfo what thou hast promised. For he has, through his great effort, the right to deserve from thee the same."

And with this, the lady began to weep bitterly, saying in reply: "The gods sever me from such a fault! This I will not so do. Rather would I rid myself of life than do a thing so displeasing to you with such a dishonor to your person."

To this the knight answered, saying: "Wife, for this matter I command that you do no injury to yourself, neither yet should you conceive any grief from such an action, for in no way shall it distress me. Go therefore, and perform that which you have given oath to, and never shall you be the whit less dear to me. But as you have fulfilled your given promise, so take you better heed of such things hereafter, even though a demanded gift may seem to you impossible to be had."

When the lady perceived that this was truly the will of her husband, she withdrew with a heavy heart and bedecked and ornamented her person to make herself most fair. Then taking her company with her, she went to Tarolfo's lodging, and blushing in her modesty and shame, presented herself to him. As soon as he saw her, Tarolfo in great surprise rose from Theban's company and greeted her with gladness, receiving her very honorably and demanding the cause of her coming. When she answered that she had come to be wholly at his will, and that he was to do with her as it so pleased him, Tarolfo answered:

"You make me wonder above measure, considering the time and the company with which you are come. This cannot be without some great alteration between you and your husband. Tell me therefore, I pray you, how the matter goes?"

The lady then told Tarolfo fully what had transpired regarding the whole matter, and when Tarolfo had heard her out, he began to think more deeply on the situation. For, as much as his admiration was increased for the lady, he also did begin to conceive a great respect for the husband who had sent his wife to him. Whosoever he be that should so much as think villainy toward such a knight, said Tarolfo to himself, would beyond doubt be worthy of the greatest blame. And, being so convinced, he spoke to the lady, saying: "Madame, like a worthy lady you have performed what was due me. And because of what you now relate to me, I account that which I desired of you as already received from your hands. And therefore, when it shall please you you may return to your husband. Do thank him on my behalf, I pray of you, for his so great a pleasure done to me, and beg of him my pardon for the folly I have thus committed against him. Assure him, that never again shall I put the like in practice."

The lady, giving great thanks to Tarolfo for such courtesy, withdrew at once in some relief from his presence and returned with her company to her husband, reciting to him in sequence all that had happened between herself and the knight Tarolfo.

Now meanwhile, Theban, presenting himself before Tarolfo, demanded how the matter stood. And when Tarolfo repeated the entire discourse to him, Theban said further: "And shall I then lose all that you have promised me?"

Tarolfo answered: "No, and when you are pleased to do so, take half of all my castles and treasures. For certainly, I have promised you this. That you have fully served my turn, I do acknowledge."

To this, Theban made reply: "It may never please the gods, but since the knight was so liberal of his wife to you and you again were not a villain to him in that offer, it would ill suit me to become less than courteous. For above all things in the world it pleases me that I have served your turn, and therefore I will that all I ought to receive in reward for my effort remain your own in such manner that it has always been." And so Theban would take nothing at all of Tarolfo.

•

The tale being finished, Menedon looked to his listeners and posed the following: "It is now questioned, in which of these actions was shown the greatest liberality or nobleness of mind? In the knight that had given liberty to his wife to go to Tarolfo; in Tarolfo who sent the lady he had always desired and for whose sake he had done so much back to her husband, free at the point of having her come to him; or in Theban who, having abandoned his country to gain the promised rewards, and having come there, did now remit the whole to Tarolfo to remain as poor as he was before?"

"Very excellent is both the tale and the demand," said the queen. "Of truth, each one was very liberal; considering the first of his honor, the second of his lascivious desire, and the third of his hoped-for riches. Great courtesy was shown all.

"Dear Menedon, if we are to decide which of them used the greatest liberality or courtesy, it is proper that we consider which of the three deeds is most acceptable. And when this has been well weighed we shall manifestly know the most liberal. For he who gives most is to be held most liberal.

"Now, of these three, the one most cherished is honor, which

Paulus Aemilius[22] in vanquishing Perses the king of Macedonia desired rather than gained treasures. The second is to be fled from, that is, the wanton delights of Venus, according to the sentence of Sophocles and of Zenocrates who has said that lust is to be avoided as a violent power. The third is not to be desired either, for riches are often troublesome to a virtuous life. And to such a one who can virtuously live with moderate poverty, so Marcus Curtius,[23] Attilius Regulus, and Valerius Publicola, do testify to it in their various works.

"If then, honor is to be held in esteem and the others not, it was he, in giving his wife to another, who used the greatest generosity, although he did behave less than wisely in doing so. He was also the most liberal, for the others did follow him in example. Therefore, according to our judgment, he who gave his wife (in whom consisted his honor) was above the rest most liberal."

"I agree," said Menedon. "Insofar as you have gone, it is as you say. But yet, each one of the others seems to me to be more liberal. And you shall hear in what manner I think it. It is very true that the first did grant his wife. But he demonstrated in so doing not so great a liberality as you speak of, for if he would have denied her, he might not justly have done so by reason of the oath she made, which was convenient for her to keep. And therefore, he who gives what he may not deny does well in making himself liberal by it, and it would seem but a trifle after all. And therefore, as I have said, each of the others was the more generous.

"As it has already been said, Tarolfo had for a long time desired this lady. He loved her far above all others. And to attain her he for a long time underwent great vicissitudes, offering himself to satisfy her request. Seeking forth things almost impossible to be had, which now obtained, he deserved through her promised faith to obtain her as well. There is no doubt that were she obtained, the honor of the husband and the release of what she promised (which he did so release) was in his hand. And so to conclude, he was then both liberal of the husband's honor and of the oath of his lady, and of his own long desire. It is a great matter to have endured long thirst and come to a pleasant fountain, and not to drink of it but to suffer others to drink.

"The third was very generous as well, considering that poverty is one of the most loathsome things of the world to bear. Putting to flight both joy and tranquillity, making off with honor and virtue, it leads only to crabbèd care, so that everyone naturally strives with a fierce desire to flee the same. A desire so magnified in many that they give themselves no less to dishonest gain than to inordinate expense, to the end that they may live splendidly in ease, not knowing or not otherwise being able to feel that their desire most often causes exile or death. How is it possible that these riches do please and are acceptable to them that in such manner are both gained and possessed of them?

"Now who would doubt that Theban was not most poor, if he were to behold how, abandoning his night's rest, he went gathering of herbs and digging up of roots in doubtful places to better sustain his meager life? And that this poverty did take possession of his virtue may also be believed, when one hears how Tarolfo was deceived as he beheld him appareled in the vilest of rags. And so desirous was he of shaking off this misery to become rich that he knowingly came as far as from Thessaly to Spain, hazarding himself to perilous chance through doubtful journey and uncertain climate, to the end that he perform the promise he had made, so that in return, he might receive these riches from another.

"Also, it may clearly be seen that without doubt he gave himself to so many mysteries in order to flee poverty by the promise of a rich life, knowing the same services to be full of grief and troubles. But for all this, he has shaken off the greatest poverty and entered the sumptuous life, for so much more is this same life acceptable to him.

"Then, he who was poor and is now become rich? If in so becoming he finds delight in it, how greater and what manner of generosity is used when he gives the same away, and consents to return to that state which he has with so much trouble fled? Assuredly, he does something of exceeding greatness and generosity. And it will seem far greater than the others when the age of the giver, now old, is also considered. For in old men, so much more does avarice become a continually pressing force than ever in the young.

"So, I do believe that each of the other two has used a greater nobleness of mind than the first so much commended by you; and the third far more so than either of the others," said Menedon in completion of his argument.

Having listened in close attention, Fiammetta now made her reply: "In how much your reasoning might well be defended by anyone else, so well is it defended by you. But we mind to show you briefly how our judgment ought to be accepted rather than your own. You will say that he showed no generosity at all, he who granted the use of his wife to another, for the reason that it was convenient that he should do so through the oath already made by his lady. Which he ought indeed do, if that oath was to be honored. But the wife, who must be considered a part of her husband, or rather, one body with him, could not justly make such an oath without the will of her husband. And yet, if she did make such an oath, it was nothing, because the first oath lawfully made could not without reason be derogated by any following; and chiefly, not by one that is not duly made for a necessary cause. And the custom is that in matrimonial unitings the man does swear to be content with the woman, and the woman with the man, and neither may change the one for another. Now then, the woman cannot swear to a thing that is not lawful. And if she does then do this contrary to the former oath, the swearing for an unlawful thing may not prevail. So, otherwise than for his own pleasure, the husband ought not to commit his wife. And if he does so commit her to Tarolfo, then it is he who is generous of his honor, and not Tarolfo as so held in your opinion. Nor can he be liberal of his oath in relinquishing it, for then the oath is nothing.

"And now we come to Tarolfo, so generous only of his wanton desire. His action was but the action of proper duty, a thing that is convenient for every man to do. We all through reason are bound to banish vice and to follow virtue. And he who does that to which by reason he is bound is, as you have said, not at all generous. Only whatever is done over and above required duty may well and justly be termed liberality. But because you perhaps argue in silence in your mind what honor may be of a chaste woman to her husband that ought to be so dear, we will prolong somewhat our talk in showing you, so that you may more clearly see in the end that Tarolfo and Theban (of whom we intend next to speak) used no generosity at all in respect of the knight.

"You shall know that chastity, together with the other virtues, yields no other reward to its possessors than its own honor. This honor, among virtuous men, makes most excellent even those of the least virtue. This honor, if men with humility seek to support it, makes them friends of God, and so by consequence to live with and in death be possessed of eternal grace. And, if a woman conserves her honor for her husband, he shall certainly live happily in security of his offspring, and may in open sight frequent among the people, content in his mind to see such virtues in his wife honored among the most high and important dames. For in his mind it is a manifest token that she is good, fearing God and loving him. Which is no small pleasure, seeing she is given him for everlasting companionship, indivisible save by death. He, through this obtained favor, is seen continually to increase both in spiritual and worldly wealth.

"And so, on the contrary, he whose wife has default of such virtues can never pass a single hour with true consolation. Nothing is acceptable to him, and each continually desires the death of the other. And through this disordered voice he perceives himself to be gossiped about by every miserly mouth in town. Nor does it seem to him that such a fault should not be believed by whomsoever it is heard. Even though she should be largely endowed with all other virtues, yet this one vice seems to have such great force as to bring her in contempt and utter ruin. Therefore this honor, which makes the woman both chaste and good to her husband, is a great gift, and is to be held most dearly. Blessed may he be called for being granted such a gift, although we believe there are but few through such grace to whom we may bear envy for so great a benefit.

"But to return to our purpose, now that it is clearly to be seen how much the knight did give. It has not fled our memory that you claim Theban to be more generous than the others. Having become enriched through great effort, he must now without question return to the misery of poor estate by giving away whatever he had gotten. It appears that you are not acquainted with poverty, which, when it comes to us with goodwill, surmounts all riches. Is it not possible that Theban by chance felt himself overcome by sundry sorry cares brought about by his newly attained wealth? Did he now imagine, perhaps, that Tarolfo, thinking himself ill-done, might by murder recover again his castles? Could he not have been abiding in fear of betrayal by his newfound tenants? It may have been that he became concerned touching the government of his lands. He now knew all the plotted guiles against his co-partner, and saw himself greatly envied for his riches, and was concerned lest thieves should secretly despoil him thereof. He was stuffed with so many such and sundry thoughts and cares that all tranquillity was fled from him. Under such influences, calling to mind that his former life passed happily without so many cares, he said to himself: I desired to grow rich, to the end that I might attain quiet rest, but I now see that it is only the source of troublesome worries and the thief of repose.

"And thereupon rendering all that was given him back to Tarolfo, he was desirous only of returning quickly to his former condition. Poverty is the refused riches, a goodness unknown, an extinguisher of provocations. All this was well understood by Diogenes. As much suffices poverty as nature requires. He lives safe from every imposture that patiently approaches therewith. Nor is he disabled from attaining great honors that his skills may earn for him, as we have already said. And therefore, as Theban rejected this allurement, he was not generous but well advised. That it did please him to return all to Tarolfo, rather than to another, was but a gracious act. He might well have bestowed the same upon many others.

"And so to conclude, the husband of the lady was more generous in offering his honor than either of the others. Remember this one thing. The honor that he gave was not to be again recovered, which happens not in many a thing, as of battles, prowess, and the like. For if at one time they are lost, they may still be recovered in another, and a return to the same state is possible. Therefore, this may suffice for the answer to your question."

THE FIFTH QUESTION
proposed by Clonico

(Which is the more unhappy? A lover who cannot obtain the favor of his mistress, or he who having obtained it has reason for jealousy?)

*And while
occupied in this pleasant employment, my eyes chanced beyond the gathering waves to a bark
coming my way with but one lone mariner and he surrounded by four gentlewomen.*

WITH THE QUEEN BECOMING SILENT AND MENEDON SAT-
isfied with her argument, a worthy young man
called Clonico by name, since he was seated after
Menedon, began speaking: "Most mighty Queen
permitting, this gentlewoman's dilemma, albeit lengthy in the telling, has so excellently been resolved that I shall now follow this tale
with small conceit but perhaps more brevity, so the others at their
own leisure may also tell us theirs." Saying this, he paused, and
looking about him with a smile, he began his story.

•

For so long as I know, being of yet enough years for experience
to have taught me this, it is apparent that those in bondage to the
young lord Eros are indeed replete with many cares and the sundry
longing provocations of love. For this reason alone with but small
delight, have I resisted for so long a time and fled the like fate. And
with valiant mind, rather eschewing than commending those who
served such a tyranny, did I well manage to escape the pitched
snares yet unsprung. Various and frequent were the temptations,
and because I was not always strong, nor could I in any way longer
resist that same force wherein Phoebus himself was unable to withstand young Cupid, I did eventually fall subject. And this before I
knew how Eros, having finally taken heart to bring me into the
circle of his victims, set about to effect his resolve and did so in the
following manner:

Walking all merry one day, being lured abroad through the
renewal of a fresh spring day, I set about for my delight to gather
shellfish strewn haphazardly upon the salt sea banks. And while
occupied in this pleasant employment, my eyes chanced beyond the
gathering waves to a bark coming my way with but one lone mari-

ner and he surrounded by four gentlewomen. Young and so fair, it was a marvelous thing to behold the beauty they did all seem to possess. I was not able once to turn my gaze from them, for in their midst I saw as they so soon and swiftly approached me a sudden and exceeding great radiance surrounding them in a golden light. In my judgment it seemed to be a figure, very young and more fair than ever I did behold. As I stood there agape with my eyes fixed steadily on his light, I imagined to have heard him address me in a voice unlike any that I had heard before: "O young fool, persecutor of our power, I come to thee in company with these four damsels each of whom you now here behold."

His craft having drawn presently closer in the shallowing waters before me, he continued: "Among these four, look well and let the eye make choice for a mistress of her that shall best suit thee."

Hearing these words so uttered I was overcome with a great fear. Hopelessly, I tried with both eye and heart to avoid what heretofore I had so many times escaped, but all was without avail for the strength in my legs did fail me. And, too, my eyes took note of bow and wings with which he most easily could overtake me in such a foolish flight.

Without further opposing his command I looked mindfully among the four lovely damsels and saw one so fair, so benign of cheer and so chaste of demeanor, that at once I thought to satisfy him by choosing her.

So singular a mistress, she could not be less, I said to myself, and it is certain this damsel presents herself most humble in my eyes. Assuredly, she will not become an enemy to my desire as so many another has before her. Nor will she scorn me at times so full of troubles, but rather shall she be the chaser away of all my vexations.

And having thought this I forthwith answered:

"O my Lord, the gracious beauty of the young damsel seated at your right hand makes me desire to be a most faithful servant both to you and to her. I am ready therefore to obey your will. Do with me now as shall best please you."

No sooner were these words spoken than I felt in my left side a wound from a shaft shot from his shining bow, which, being held aloft, I saw to be of gold. Turning then to the one of my choice I saw him strike her with another, not of gold, however, as was assuredly the first, but what I believed to be lead.

So, in this manner was I taken and caught in his snare that for so long a time I had contrived to evade. And it is most certain that from the moment of this curious happening the young woman pleased my eye so well, all other pleasures became scarce in comparison to it.

But now, well content in her notice of this and knowing me to be so well taken with my delight as not to love her was a thing impossible, she began a display of guile toward me with an ill-deserved disdain. Incontinent in behavior she showed herself a most cruel enemy, turning her eye as she happened to spy me, always contrary with words of dispraise, undeserved on my part. All this cruelty, by occasion of which in sundry ways both with prayers and humility, I have attempted to appease, but in no way succeeding. With frequent tears and lamentations at my misfortune I find myself quite unable to withdraw from loving her. Instead, how much more I find her cruel so much more do I think the flame of her pleasure sets my heart on fire.

Bewailing with infinite sighs and many tears these things that I relate, there came upon me one day all solitary in a garden a singular friend to whom part of my griefs were therein discovered.

He began to comfort me the best he could with charitable words, but giving him no ear at all I answered only that my misery exceeded all others. And to this he made me the reply: "A man is so much more miserable as he makes or accounts himself wretched. Believe me, assuredly I know of another with greater cause to lament than you."

Turning disdainfully away I answered with an angry look: "And how? Who can have greater cause than I? For good service do I not receive evil recompense? Is not my faithful love rewarded only with hatred? It is possible another can be as sorrowful as I, but more so he cannot be."

"Truly," said my friend, "it is I who have greater cause for grief than you, so hear me out. It must not be unknown to you that I for some time and to this moment have a great love for a certain gentlewoman. Furthermore, as you well know, I spared neither my wit nor power to bring about anything I thought might please her.

"And truly, when she understood what I most desired she most compliantly made me a gracious gift of it. Now this I have received, as I readily admit, and receiving it whenever it pleases me I thought that no one in any way did have so comparably joyous a life to equal mine. Yet one thing did prick me. In no way could I make her believe how perfectly I loved her. Moreover, she, perceiving me to love her as I said, passed it off lightly for a thing of little consequence.

"The gods grant no worldly good turn without some bitterness as well. To the end that the heavenly may better be appreciated and more resolutely desired, they, to this small goad, further afflicted me with a distress annoying beyond comparison.

"One day, as I lay with her all alone in a secret place and seeing, without ourselves being seen, all those who passed by, it happened there came near to our hiding place a proper young man of pleasant countenance, whom she at once beheld with impassioned eye. This I perceived, and more, for when he had passed from our view she fetched so pitiful a sigh I could but hardly forebear and said to her: 'Alas, do you so soon repent that now for the love of another you do sigh?'

"With face all aflame and swearing by the power of the high gods she attempted with many excuses to make me believe the contrary of what I had observed. But because my heart was kindled with a furious anger, this was to no purpose for she made me almost ready then to chide with her. Instead, I withdrew from her in silence. And certainly it will never be out my mind but that she loves him or some other better than me. All those persuasions that previously she used to convince me that she loved me beyond any other, I now esteem to be the contrary. Imagining that whatever had passed between us was said and done on her part with complaisance I can find neither prevailing comfort nor my intolerable grief endurable. Because shame does often bridle the will, I would rather you pity than cheer me, so that I do not continue my bitter grief nor make any appearance of doing so. In brief, I am never without cares and deep thoughts that bring far greater unhappiness than I would have it so. Learn then to bear the lesser griefs since you see the greater with valiant mind borne by me."

To this I answered that his grief though great seemed in no way compared to mine. He answered then the contrary. And so it went in long contention and eventually we parted without any settlement.

•

With this tale now completed, Clonico turned to Fiammetta and said: "I pray of you that you will here give us with just reason your judgment on this."

The queen answered: "Young gentleman, it is without question that your pain is great. And great wrong does the damsel commit in not loving you. Still, by hope your grief may be eased. But this can never happen to your companion, for once he is entered by suspicion nothing is able to draw it away. So long as his love endures he suffers without comfort. Therefore the grief of him who is jealous must in our judgment be greater than that of the unloved lover."

Then, Clonico spoke in turn: "O noble Queen, because you say so, it is plain to see that you have been loved always by the one whom you love in return. And if this be true, you can hardly know what my pain is. How can it be that jealousy brings greater grief than what I feel, inasmuch as the jealous one continues still to possess the one whom he desires? In one hour he may take more delight in holding her than I feel pain for so long as I cannot. Also, he may through experience abandon such jealousy if it happens that his suspicions prove false. On the other hand, being kindled with a fiery desire and assaulted by a thousand incitements, the more I see myself deprived of attainment the more I burn and consume myself in consequence. Because I live in such desperation there is no longer any help for it. The more frequently I reprove her the sharper each hour she becomes. For this reason alone your answer seems contrary to the truth. I do not question but that it is much better to hold with suspicion than to desire alone in tears."

To this the queen then answered: "Truly, as you affirm, the amorous flame that shines in our eyes and each hour adorns our sight with greater beauty never consents that we love in vain. On the other hand, to say that we do not know how great and what manner of pain you suffer we do protest. As our answer has been strengthened by whatever is true, one thing more will we show you.

"Clearly it is seen that those things most hindering the quiet of the mind are cares, even though some come to a merry end and others we see ending with great sorrow. When the mind is most replete with concern so much more has it of grief, and especially is it so when this is oppressive. It is surely most certain that the jealous one has a greater abundance of this than you. On the other hand, all that is needed to free you of your grief, and nothing else, is gaining the goodwill of the damsel whom you love. Not to be able to attain this may seem a grief most hurtful, but yet it is possible that it might easily come to pass. Inconstancy of a woman's heart may in one instant make the same attainable. Indeed, she might already love you, and in waiting for proof that you love her also, show the contrary until such time as she shall be well assured of your love. With such thoughts can hope mitigate grief.

"But the jealous one has fully laden his mind with infinite terrors, against which neither hope nor any other delight can bring comfort to ease the pain. For there he stands intently demanding a right to the wandering eye, which its possessor cannot give; and by his every action dictating laws for the feet, the hands, and for each different act of his mistress. He will be a watchful master both of his thought and disposition, interpreting everything in evil part toward himself, believing that each and every one desires her whom he alone loves. He imagines her every spoken word as well to be full of deceit and double meaning. And if he ever commits a slander toward her it is death for him to remember it, imagining himself deceived instead by his very own distraction. He will by conjecture shut off the ways of the air and the earth with its beasts, as well as the heavens, the birds, and every other creature he thinks hinders his desires. And to remove himself from this is a hopeless task, for in so doing and at the same time finding the woman faithful he thinks that she sees what he is doing and is suspicious of him for it.

"If he finds good reason for his jealousy he pretends not to see it. And who then is more dolorous than he? If by chance you think that embracing her in his arms is so great a delight as to mitigate these pangs for him your judgment is in fault. For thinking that others as well as he have embraced her in the like sort infects his mind's ease, and he becomes afflicted with choler. Now, should the woman by chance lovingly entertain him, he suspects at once that she does it only for the purpose of removing such imaginations he may have of her and not for the true love that in reality she bears him. If he finds her maliciously disposed he thinks that she then loves another and is no longer content with him.

"Thus we can show you an infinite number of other suspicions and cares that are harbored in a jealous person. What shall we say then of his life but that it is far more grievous than that of any other living creature. He lives, believing and not believing, and still he is attracted to the woman. It happens more often than not that these jealous persons do end their lives through this selfsame malice of which they live in fear. And not without cause, for through such censures they show the way to self-injury.

"Consider then all these reasons. Your jealous friend to his sorrow has more cause than you, for you at least have hope of attaining still, while he lives in constant fear of losing what he scarcely holds for his own. And therefore, if he has more cause for grief than you and yet comforts himself the best he can, how much more ought you to comfort yourself and set aside your lamentations that befit only the faint of heart. Hope instead that the assured love you bear toward your lady shall not lose its due reward. For though she shows herself sharp toward you at this moment it cannot be but that she loves you, in that this lady has yet to excuse herself from the obligation your own love has set upon her. And you know yourself that stubborn oaks are sooner broken by fierce and vehement winds than are consenting reeds."

THE SIXTH QUESTION
proposed by a young Gentlewoman in black

(Two maidens in love with the same youth wish to induce him to choose between them. Agreed on this, one runs to him, embraces him and kisses him; the other cannot but remain apart, all shy and shameful. Which of them loved him better or deserved his love more?)

The two young gentlewomen being thus determined in their resolve began to run their race, and my brother espying them and seeing in what manner they came toward him marveled greatly.

NOW, NEXT TO CLONICO WAS SEATED A FAIR YOUNG GENTLE-
woman gowned in flowing gossamer over a garment of
black. Perceiving the queen to have made an end to her
words she in her turn began to speak:

•

Most gracious Queen, once when I was a little girl, I remember
how one day in a garden I met with my brother alone, without other
company. Of riper years and comely in person, my brother tarrying
there awhile and amusing me in childish games, did not as I did,
observe two young damsels of noble blood and abounding in riches
looking down upon us from another terrace. Both were born in our
city, and it was known to me that both loved my brother very much.
Perceiving him to be in this garden, they came closer and from a
distance began without his knowledge to contemplate upon the
comeliness of his person.

And after a while, seeing him alone save for me with whom
they did not reckon because I was little, one of them began to speak
thus and so to the other: "We two love this young gentleman above
all others, with neither of us knowing whether he loves us or not.
Yet it is possible that he can love us both. Because he is alone, it is
now opportune to satisfy our desire and discover whether he loves
either of us, or which of us he loves best. To the end that she whom
he shall best like may remain his from this day forward without
hindrance of the other, let us run to him and each one embrace and
kiss him. In this way we shall declare ourselves and he shall decide
once and for all which of us best pleases him."

The two young gentlewomen being thus determined in their
resolve began to run their race, and my brother espying them and
seeing in what manner they came toward him marveled greatly. But

one of them stayed suddenly a good way from us, and there stood bashful almost to the point of weeping. The other continued the race, and coming upon him she embraced and kissed him and sat down beside him, recommending herself all the while to his favor.

And he, the astonishment conceived of her boldness now somewhat diminished, entreated her, as ever she loved him, to tell him truly what moved them thus to behave so. She concealed nothing from him and he, mindful of all that he heard, and what the one and the other had done, knew not which of them best loved him nor how to persuade himself which of them he might best love.

So happening at that moment to see me all restless and impatient, he excused himself, took my hand, and departed from them. Later, in counsel with many of his friends on this matter he was not able to satisfy in any way his desire on this demand. For which cause I now pray you, from whom I assuredly believe to come a true definition of my question, tell me which of these two damsels ought soonest to have been loved of the young man?

•

To the gentlewoman all dressed in black, the queen made answer in this manner: "Truly it seems to me, of the two young women, she loved your brother best and soon ought to be loved by him in return who in bashful doubting waited without embracing him. And I give you this reason:

"Love, as we well know, makes those in whom he does abide always fearful. And where he is of greatest force, there rests likewise the greatest fear. This happens because the intent or consent of the person loved can never be fully known. And if it could be known, many things would be done that are left undone for fear of offense, because one knows that, in displeasing, all occasion to be loved is taken away. Now with this fear and love, shamefastness is always accompanied, and not without reason.

"Returning then to our question, we say that it was an act of one unfeignedly enamored, that of the gentlewoman who showed herself both fearful and bashful, whereas the behavior of the other did reveal only the action of one both lewd and licentious. And therefore he, being of the first best beloved, ought certainly in our judgment to love her best."

To this argument the gentlewoman then made her reply: "Most courteous Queen, it is true that where love abides with moderation, there fear and bashfulness do also frequent. But where love does abound in such quantity that it takes away sight from the most wise, as is already said, then I say that fear has no place there. Instead, bold action and strong feeling are in equal proportion to him who urges them forward. And therefore, that gentlewoman seeing her desire before her eyes was so hotly kindled that she, abandoning all shamefulness, ran straight to him who so vehemently moved her beyond all endurance.

"The other, not so much inflamed and observing the amorous rules, remained bashfully behind, as you say. So it must be that she who ran loved most, and most ought to be loved in return."

"Discreet Gentlewoman," said the queen, "true it is that excessive love takes away the sight and every other proper defense in things that are against his nature, but not in those that truly belong to him, which as love increases, so do they. Then how much greater a quantity of love is found in anyone you so much the more fear.

"That this is true, the wounded heart of Byblis does show plainly enough by the sequel thereof to her greater love. For seeing herself abandoned and refused she had not the audacity to show herself as she really was, but disclosed her unfitting desire in writing.

"Likewise, Phaedra[24] many times attempted to go to Hippolytus, to whom she thought boldly to speak and tell how much she loved him. But the words she had to utter no sooner came into her mouth than they stayed upon her tongue and there died.

"O how fearful is the person that loves! Who has been more mighty than Alcydes,[25] so little satisfied by the victory of human things that he also gave himself to hold up the heavens. And notwithstanding this, was lastly enamored not of a woman but of a wench, a slave that he had won in a wager. So afraid was he of her commandments, he did for her even the very basest of things, like any humble subject or servant. Also Paris, in what he dared not attempt either with eye or tongue in the presence of his love, with his finger in wine that had been spilt, wrote first her name, and after —*I love thee.*

"Surpassing all these, Pasiphaë brings us a true example of fear. She, who without any direction of mind, yes, and without understanding, dared not even express her desire to a beast. Instead, gathering for him the tender grass with her own gentle hands, she endeavors to make him favorable to her and to kindle the same desire in him that was in her, ofttimes bedecking herself before the glass for his pleasure so that in the end he might seek what she dared not demand.

"It is not proper for an enamored woman, nor for any other, to be forward and easy. For as much as this great shamefastness that ought always to be in us does remain, it is the guardian of our honor. It is said among men that we know better than they how to hide the amorous flame, and in truth this is so. Nothing else in us engenders this but the great fear which does occupy our forces rather than those of men. How many have there been of these (and peradventure we have known some) who so often have caused themselves to be bidden and thereby achieve the amorous effects, who would rather have bidden the bidder before he them if due bashfulness and fear had not detained them? And not only this, but every time 'no' escapes their mouths, they have had in their minds a thousand repentings, saying 'yes' from their hearts a thousand times.

"There remains also the same scarlet fire that, for Semiramis[26] and Cleopatra who loved only to quiet the rage of their wanton wills, once being satisfied was then forgotten in an instant. Wise merchants unwillingly do venture all their treasure at one time to the hazards of Fortune. And yet, notwithstanding that, they think nothing of risking some small portion which, if they happen to lose, gives them no grief of mind at all.

"The young woman, therefore, who embraced your brother loved him but little. And in committing that little to Fortune, she most likely said: 'If I may hereby get this gentleman it is well, but if he refuses me, that is that and let him take another.'

"The other, behaving in so bashful a manner, hesitated to place so great a love in hazard, thinking that if this love she bore him should displease him and he refuse her, her grief then would be so great that she should die thereof.

"Let therefore the second be loved before the first."

THE SEVENTH QUESTION
proposed by Galeone

(Is love a good or an evil thing? A question containing a charming ballad in which is explained the sense of the name of Fiammetta.)

Beyond the splendor it brought to her face, it so light-
ened the place that in the fresh shade it yielded a marvelous luster to the whole company.

a CLEAR SUNBEAM PIERCING THROUGH AMONGST THE GREEN leaves did suddenly strike upon the aforesaid fountain and rebound then its light upon the face of the adorned queen. Instantly she was appareled in that color of which the heavens make show, as if both the children of Latona,[27] suddenly hidden from us, were with their stars alone to give us light. Beyond the splendor it brought to her face, it so lightened the place that in the fresh shade it yielded a marvelous luster to the whole company.

Furthermore, for a moment, the reflected ray extended even to that place where the laurel crown rested and clearly defined the falling golden tresses. It so intermingled with the natural twinings that at first sight one would have said there had issued forth among the green leaves a clear flame of burning fire, spreading in such a way that the auburn ringlets were easily seen by all who stood about.

Galeone, seated in the circle opposite the queen and divided from her only by the water, was by chance sooner and better aware of this marvelous sight than any of the others. He very attentively beheld all this, almost as if he cared for nothing else. Now that his turn was come, the question went begging from his silent lips.

The queen having waited in silence a good while, as all this certainly pleased the understanding woman, at last interrupted his reverie by speaking:

"Perhaps it is a longing for something that you behold that stays you. Tell us what is the occasion that holds you thus stunned? In following the order of the rest, it is now your turn and you speak not. In truth, we believe it is mindless gazing about our head, as if you had never seen the same before. Tell us first, and afterward, as the others have so propounded their questions, propound yours."

At this sudden interruption Galeone, lifting up his mind so recently filled with sweet wandering thoughts, and somewhat coming to himself as was his habit when a sudden fear would break his golden sleep, said: "Most noble and renowned Queen, whose worthiness it should be impossible for me to declare, as I so intently gazed upon yourself, my mind did become enraptured by a particular and gracious thought. Beholding the bright ray that streamed into the cool freshet, rebounding and reflecting upon your face, I imagined there issued forth from the water a little sprite, all gentle and gracious to look upon. And as my mind was plucked back to behold this image (my eyes being altogether insufficient to scan so great a joy), he mounted on this crystal ray and took residence within your eyes. There for a happy moment he made marvelous mirth, adorning your glance with extraordinary clarity. Then leaving his footfall in your eyes to mount even higher, I saw how he ascended by the light to rest upon your crown. And there, together with the ray, he kindled anew in my imagination such a flame as was once seen by Tanaquil[28] to appear over the sleeping Servius Tullius[28] when he was still but an infant child.

"And so it went about your crown, leaping from sprig to sprig like a small, amorous bird, that singing visits many blossoms, moving your heart with his sundry gestures, sometimes wrapping and hiding himself therein and being merrier every time he comes forth thereof. And now he became so jocund, it seemed to me everything became nothing, out of which there came a song, a sweet voice singing. And these were its words:

> Of the third rolling sky, the benign babe divine
> I am, enamored so, to nest in these two eyne,

That doubtless die I should, were I of mortal rout:
From twig to twig I twine, to feed this my delight,
These golden tresses whirling in and out:
Myself, inflaming myself, right
So as with flame I show the effect, the potent might
Of my darts divine, piercing where I go,
Each one wounding, that with sweet sight,
Does gaze her in the eyes, whereas each hour loe,
If such her pleasure be, I there descend a down,
For of my kingdoms she Queen is of great renown . . .

"And here, he would have said more as he went about, but you called out to me. And you had no sooner spoken than he suddenly retired into your eyes, which, sparkling like the Morning Star, gave off such a radiance as to make the entire place shine. You have heard now with what joy new thoughts have sustained me for a time."

Filocolo and the others marveled not a little at what they had just heard, and turning toward their queen at once saw for themselves all that in description had seemed impossible. And she, rapt by the words that were truly reported of her, all attired with humility and sitting with steadfast countenance, made no answer at all.

Galeone with a gesture of his hand caught once again the attention of each, and now, in turn speaking more gravely, followed right afterward with this question:

"Gracious Queen, this I desire you to tell; whether or not a man ought to be enamored for his delight alone? Many things prompt me, both seen and heard and held among the various opinions of others, to ask such of you."

Looking directly into his face the queen observed Galeone for some time. She sighed in a peculiar manner and began her reply:

"It is appropriate to speak out against what we desire to follow. And truly, the answer to the question you propound with such perplexity ought to be obvious. In answering you therefore, let us begin in the proper order.

"So that his indignation does not fall upon us, may he whose subjects we are forgive us these words. Words that even so are constrained through force of judgment shall yet unwillingly be used against Love's divine majesty. And you that are his subjects as well as we, give ear to them with a bold mind, and not for any reason at all be deflected from this resolution.

"If upon occasion we digress from our subject, we shall turn again to it as conveniently as possible, that you may better understand the more apparent design of our words. So let us now continue.

"Love is of three sorts through which all things are loved. Some through the virtue of one, and some through the power of another. But all depends upon the thing loved and likewise the lover.

"The first of the three is called honest love. This is the good, upright, and loyal love. And surely above all else is this the due of every person. It is what holds the high and first Creator linked to His creatures, and by it are they tied to Him. Through it the heavens, the world, realms, provinces, and cities abide and continue undiminished. And through it we merit the eternal possession of the celestial kingdom; for without it we lose the power of doing good.

"The second is called love for delight, and certainly it is this to which we are most subject. This is our god to whom we pray, trusting that he may be our gratification, bringing fulfillment of all our desires. And herein is put the question to which we shall duly return.

"The third is love for utility. Of this the world is supplied more fully than any other thing. Coupled with Fortune, wherever she tarries it likewise abides. But if parted from Fortune such love is the ruin then of many virtues. And to speak unreasonably, it ought to be considered more as hate than love.

"Now, as touching on the propounded question, we need speak no further of the first or of the last. But we will speak of the second, that is, of love for delight, to whom truly no person who desires to lead a virtuous life ought submit himself. For it is the depriver of honors, a troublemaker, unveiler of vices, and the general contributor of hopeless anxieties. It steals away the liberty of others, a thing above all else to be held most dear. What is he then, who in wisdom and caring for his own welfare will not flee such a power? Let him that may live free to follow these things that in every way increase his liberty, leave to vicious governors the governing of vicious vassals."

Galeone to this then replied: "I did not intend by my question to diminish in any way our disport, nor to make uneasy the regiment of our lord Eros, nor again to trouble the minds of any others. I did rather imagine by your definition, according to the intent of me and many others, that you might give new assurance to those that are his subjects with a valiant mind, and invite those that with a greedy appetite are not. But I see your purpose is contrary to mine.

"By your definition you show that there are three sorts of love. And of these, the first and last, I do agree, are as you say. But the second, which describes what I ask, you say is as much to be fled as

I believe it is to be followed. In it, is there not the promise of a glorious consummation?

"That it is the increaser of virtue, I hope to make apparent to you by all that follows. Thus love, of which we reason, does work this property in human hearts, that once disposing the mind to a thing that pleases it, spoils the same of all pride and all fierceness, humbling its victim in the doing. And this must be clearly evident to all the world as it is to ourselves, for we have found it so from our own experience. In loving Venus did not Mars, so fierce and sharp a leader in battle, become most humble and pleasant a lover?

"Are not the greedy and covetous made liberal and courteous? Medea, that most careful guardian of her magical arts, exposed to Cupid's flames, did liberally yield up herself, her honor, and all her arts to Jason. Who is it that makes men more diligent to impossible ventures, but this master of delight? What he is capable of may be found in the histories of Paris and Menelaus. Again, who further fans the angry fires more than he? He shows us how the anger of Achilles was often quieted through the sweet pleadings of Polyxena.[29]

"He above all others makes men courageous and strong. I know not what greater example may be given than that of Perseus,[30] who, for the love of Andromeda, did make a marvelous proof of his virtuous force. All that are appareled by him are decked with excellent qualities, with ornate talk, with magnificence, and with pleasantness. He, I say, bestows upon all his subjects fineness and gentleness. O, how many are the good things that proceed from love!

"Who moved Virgil? Who, Ovid? Who of the other poets who have won eternal fame by their holy verses, but he? Without him they should never have come to our ears.

"What shall we say further of Love's virtues but that he was able to give Orpheus'[31] harp such a sweetness when he called forth its sound as to still the rustling leaves and make stay the running streams. Its power was such that into the presence of Orpheus came fierce lions together in mild peace with the fainthearted hinds and all other beasts. It made likewise the infernal Furies quiet, giving rest and sweetness to the troubled souls. But above all this, the sound was of such virtue that Orpheus regained his lost Eurydice.

"No, Love is not the destroyer of honor as you say, nor the source of untimely trouble, nor the instigator of vices, nor the disposer of unworthy cares. Neither is he the worthless abuser of the liberty of others. Anyone that is not his servant, nor yet made accountable to him, ought with all wit and diligence work to attain the favor of such a lord, for in becoming his subject one surely then becomes virtuous.

"Whatever pleases the gods and men of greatest strength ought likewise to please us as well. Let such a lord therefore be loved, served, and live always in our minds."

"Misguided Galeone, greatly deceived are you in your opinion," answered Fiammetta. "And it is no wonder, because so far as we understand, you are enamored beyond all hope. Without doubt, the judgment of the enamored is absolutely false. Having lost sight of the mind's eye, so too have they banished reason as their utter enemy. And for this cause alone, it is proper for us to speak out against Love. This we do unwillingly and in grief, since we are his subject too. But yet, to draw you from your error we shall turn our silence to a true report and insist that you understand; for this love you defend is nothing less than unreasonable desire sprung from a passion that enters the heart through wanton pleasure. It is opened to the eyes and nourished with idleness by the memory and thoughts of foolish minds. And the more it increases, the more it takes away interest from things necessary and disposes the same into things unprofitable.

"But because you through various given examples endeavor to show that only goodness and virtue do proceed from love, we will proceed to disprove your proofs. It is no part of humility for a man to take whatever belongs to another, but rather an arrogance and an unseemly presumption. It is just that which Mars,[32] whom you make to be so humble in love, assuredly used in taking from Vulcan his most lawful wife, Venus.

"And without doubt, this humility that appears in the face of lovers does not proceed from a benign heart, but takes root in guile and deceit. Nor does this love make the covetous liberal, as you describe Medea to be. Deprived of all reason by love, she at once foolishly became prodigal of things dearly esteemed, not giving the same with measure but unprofitably casting them away. In so doing she believed she pleased, but instead displeased. Medea, learning nothing from this prodigality, soon repented her useless effort, and learned too late that if she had used those dear gifts modestly, she should not have come to so vile an end.

"Soliciting that takes advantage of or does injury to the solicitor ought not to be sought for in our opinion. For how much better it is to stand idle than to work harm; although neither one nor the other is to be praised. Paris was the agent of his own destruction though he might well have anticipated the results of his heedless soliciting. And the reason for Menelaus[8] becoming suddenly diligent was not for love; it was to recover his lost honor, a thing that any prudent person ought well to do.

"Neither is the love we speak of a means to mitigate anger. It is simple goodness of mind that remits the offense. The brunt that induces anger passes and makes it become nothing. Yet lovers and discreet persons, accustomed to the prayers of the beloved to forgive offenses, good-naturedly do so only to be courteous to whatever costs them nothing, and makes those in need of forgiveness beholden to them. In this way Achilles many times expelled from his heart congealed anger.

"You say in your argument that love for delight makes men courageous and worthy. But in this I can show you the contrary. Who was a man of greater valor than Hercules? And yet, enamored, he became indeed vile and forgetful of his power so that he spun thread with the women of Omphale,[33] assuredly an unheroic action that incurred little danger.

"When most hardy people become enamored and danger threatens, they show themselves brave and put themselves forward; not because of love as you think, but because their little wit lures them to do so, to the end that they will seem more glorious in the sight of their loves. However, it happens very seldom, because they so concern themselves over the separation from the person loved that, rather than give themselves to peril, they become content to be held mean and of little courage.

"We do not question at all the claim that through this love reposes all the sweetness in Orpheus' harp. We agree that this is true as you have shown. Yet truly, in general, love loads the tongues of its subjects with such a sweetness and with so many enticements that they would more often than not make the stones turn upside down. So that to entice is not only the property of wavering and inconstant men but of worthless men too. How shall we say? That such a lord ought to be followed through the good example of the follower? Assuredly one in whom love abides, makes wise and profitable counsels to be despised. When things went badly for the Trojans, still the counsels of Cassandra[34] were not heard by Paris.

"Love also makes his subjects forgetful and careless of their good fame. More than all else, ought fame to remain after our deaths as eternal heir to the memory of us on earth. And how much did these aforesaid subjects condemn the same? Aegisthus may serve as an example, although Scylla[35] wrought no less hurt than did Pasi-phaë.

"Is not Love the occasion that breaks the sacred bonds of a promised pure faith? Yes truly, what had Ariadne[36] done to her sovereign Theseus that he, contaminating the matrimonial banns and giving himself and his promised faith to the winds, should abandon her in misery among the desert rocks? A little pleasure in gazing into the eyes of Phaedra was the occasion that accelerated so much evil, and the only recompense for the received honor. In him also is found no law. Again, that I speak the truth may be seen by the doings of Tereus[37] who, having received Philomela from her pitiful father and carnally known her, hesitated not at all to con-taminate the most holy matrimonial laws contracted between him-self and Procne the sister of Philomela. This also, calling and caus-ing himself to be called a god, occupies the thoughts of the gods.

"What words could ever fully describe the iniquities of such a one? I will tell you in simple words. Those that follow Love will be lead by him to all evils. If, by chance, his followers perform any virtuous acts (which happens very seldom) they do so with premedi-tated and corrupt desire, to the end that their loathsome wills be fully satisfied as quickly as possible. Such virtues might rather be called vices, for what man does must never be considered singly. Think instead with what mind it is done, and accord it so to the will of the worker. Never from an evil root sprang a good tree, nor from an evil tree good fruit. This Love then is lewd and naught. And if it be naught then is Love to be fled, for whoever flees things that are evil will follow the good, and in consequence, be both good and virtuous.

"The beginning of this love is none other than fear, the sequel is sin, and the evil thereof is grief and nothingness. It ought then to be fled and to be reproved. Fear to have him in you for he is violent, and no one knows of what excesses he is capable, so devoid is he of all reason. He is without doubt the destroyer of the mind. The shame, anguish, passion, grief, and complaint of the same never consents that the heart wherein he lodges be without bitterness. Who but fools will then encourage that Love be followed?

"Truly, if it were lawful we would willingly live without Love. But of such a harm we are too late aware. And since we are caught in his nets, therefore until the light that guided Aeneas out of the dark ways as he fled the perilous fires may appear to us, it is better for us to follow him and be guided submissively to his pleasures."

THE EIGHTH QUESTION
proposed by a young Gentlewoman named Paola

(Of two women whom he likes equally, ought a young man prefer her who is of superior station to him, by noble birth, parentage, and riches?)

And we never doubt in these situations that the honor of either the greatest or the meanest of women is well looked to by some of their kinfolk, regardless of position.

SEATED ON THE RIGHT HAND OF GALEONE WAS A FAIR GENTLE-woman named Paola. She was agreeable and openly pleasant; her manner in truth served only to conceal a guileless and simple soul. Presently, observing the queen to have regained once more her composure, she began her say in this fashion: "O noble Lady; you have decreed among these present that no person ought to follow Love, who is surely our true master and lord. And I for my part do consent to this. But still, it would seem impossible to me that the youthful race be run either by man or maid without this gentle Love.

"Setting apart, by your leave, your sentence, I gather even so that to be enamored is lawful, and indeed, to accept the evil doing is the appropriate action. Now in following the same I desire to know this of you: Which of two women, both pleasing, ought a young man choose for his beloved? Either she who is of noble blood and of worthy family, so plentifully endowed as to exceed many times the fortune of the suitor; or another that is neither rich nor of high birth, nor yet of kindred so abounding as is the young man?"

The queen made answer in this manner: "Fair Gentlewoman, admitting the argument that both man and woman ought to follow in the pursuit of Love, as we have elsewhere affirmed, we are of the opinion that in how much the woman is richer, greater, and more noble than the young man of whatsoever degree or dignity, even so, she ought rather to be preferred as his beloved than another who has anything less than he.

"Because man's mind was created to follow high things, he therefore must seek to advance rather than in any way debase himself. Further, there is a common proverb that says:

> The good to covet better 'tis,
> Than to possess that which bad is.

For which cause, in our judgment, it is better that one love the more noble and, with good reason, refuse the less noble."

In pleasant reply Paola again spoke: "Noble Queen, I would have given another judgment if it had been my choice in the matter, as you shall hear.

"We all naturally do rather prefer our troubles to be short and brief to those that are long and tedious. That it is easier and of more brief trouble to get the love of the less noble than that of the other is a common truth. Clearly then, the less ought to be followed; for as much as the love of the less may be said to be already won, the love of the more noble is yet to get. Furthermore, many perils may follow a man who aspires to a woman of greater condition than himself. And indeed, does he gain thereby any greater delight than he will receive from the lesser?

"A woman of position and great family is surrounded by many kinsmen who keep a constant eye to her; each and all diligently attendant of her honor. So yet if any one of them happens to suspect this love, great peril, as we have already said, may thereby follow the lover. And this cannot so easily be suffered by one less exalted. He ought to flee this peril while he is able, for harm from such is surely to come. And he who shall do it will laugh, himself, afterward in scorn, saying that it served him well. Where he is more welcome, let him go there for love.

"Yet dies he more than once? How that happens, where, and for what occasion besides, each one ought to take good heed.

"Now too, it is to be believed that a gentlewoman will esteem him but lightly, for she may well expect to be the beloved of one more noble or greater than herself and not of one inferior to herself. This in itself may seldom or never allow him to attain his desire. But to one of lesser fortune the contrary shall happen. She will glory to be loved of such a lover and will strive only to please him to the end that love be nourished. Even if this were not the case, the power of the lover alone might, without fear, effect the fulfillment of his desire.

"And so for this reason, I gather that a maiden of humble degree ought to be preferred in love before one who is more privileged."

"Your judgment misleads you," said the queen to the fair Paola, "because it is in the nature of love that how much more the one loves so much the more he desires to love. And it troubles him not a little. It may seem the greater grief is felt through love, yet in truth he loves continually all the more.

"Nor does anyone in his heart desire so speedy a conquest, although he may make of it a great appearance in words. As small troubles are sought by the slothful, so, to the wise, things that are attained with greater effort are held most dear and delightful. And therefore, he, in loving the lesser of the two, should have little trouble getting her, but in this action he would appear to desire only less and less of love. As we have said, this is contrary to the nature of love.

"But in loving the greater who has been wooed with much effort the contrary is true. In a thing dearly gotten with travail there reposes all diligence to the well-heeding of the gained love. For every hour that finds her the more beloved, there the delight and pleasure continues to a longer degree.

"And yet, if you then say your greater concern is of the kinsmen, we will not deny it. This is one of the occasions in which there can be trouble to the man who forms an attachment with a person of high station. However, the merits in such cases proceed in mysterious ways. A fool may come by misadventure loving one of low degree as well as the other. And we never doubt in these situations that the honor of either the greatest or the meanest of women is well looked to by some of their kinfolk, regardless of position. But whatever he shall do to those who love him, it will pass in cruelty Pisistratus,[38] who, without thinking first of the consequences as he should have done, offended those that loved him.

"In saying also that loving a woman of greater estate than one's own will be no limit to one's desire you show yourself to be ignorant. For should the woman covet the love of one greater than herself in position, she will instead hold him then in no esteem at all. But even the least of men, in whom some natural virtue must be found, is of greater and better circumstance than herself. For the virtuous or vicious life often makes great one of low estate, and likewise reduces the great to the meanest level. Therefore, should any woman be solicited by any man of due sort, beyond question let her yield to his desire, even though she is of greater degree and more effort than the man. For in truth, we see the continual fall of soft water break and pierce the hard stone.

"And therefore, let none despair of love. For much goodness shall follow him who loves and engages himself to please a woman greater than himself, in decent qualities, in the company of noble personages, in boldness of enterprise, and in splendor of apparel. So then, if he shall attain to greater glory, the greater delight he shall have of mind. Likewise, he shall be exalted with the good report of the people, and reputed to be of a noble mind. Let him follow the one of highest degree, as we have already said."

THE NINTH QUESTION
proposed by Feramonte, duke of Montorio

*(Who is it better that
a young man should love: a maiden, a married woman, or a widow?)*

There is no way left readier to them that, to despite their husbands, they give their love to another by whom they are attracted, and receive of him the same in return.

NEXT TO THE AMIABLE GENTLEWOMAN CALLED PAOLA SAT FERA-
monte, duke of Montorio, who, after the queen had
spoken, began: "I am of the same mind, that if it is lawful
to love at all, you have already given full reply to this
gentlewoman's question. And, that a man ought rather to love a
more noble person than one of lesser degree may very well be
yielded to through the various reasons you have shown. But, forasmuch as there are not a few gentlewomen of various and sundry
sorts adorned with a diversity of habits who do love, some more,
some less, some more hotly, and some others more lukewarm, I do
desire to understand of you which of three persons a young man
ought soonest to be enamored of? Should he either choose her who
is already married, or the young and virgin damsel, or the widow
to bring his desire to a most happy end?"

To this the queen did reply with promptness:

"Of the three, the first who is the married woman ought in no
wise be desired. For she is not her own nor has she the liberty to
give of herself elsewhere. And therefore to desire her or to take her
is both to commit an offense against the divine law and the natural
and positive laws as well; the offending of which is to heap upon
ourselves divine anger and by consequence heavy judgment. However, he who probes not his conscience too far inwardly does often
succeed better in the loving of this one than of the other two, either
maid or widow. Although such love is sometimes accompanied with
much peril, more often than not he consummates his desire. And
why this is so, the bringing of a lover more frequently to his desire,
I give you now the reason.

"It is a certainty that in how much the fire is fanned so much
the more it flames, and without the blowing it becomes dead. As all

other things decay through much use, so contrariwise is lust; the more it is used the more it increases and brighter grows its flame.

"Being a long time deprived of love and without the like effect, the widow feels almost as though it had never been, and her love is more or less kindled by memory rather than concupiscence. Also, the maiden who has yet no skill and knows of the same only in her imagination desires, as it were, one lukewarm. So, truly, it is the married woman more than any of the others who, kindled in such passions, does wish for the experience of love.

"On occasion the married are wont to receive from their husbands outrageous words and deeds for which they would willingly take revenge if they might. There is no way left readier to them than that, to despite their husbands, they give their love to another by whom they are attracted, and receive of him the same in return. And although it is expedient that such manner of revenge be very secret so no shame can grow thereby, nevertheless they are quite satisfied in their own minds. Further, the constant serving of one kind of meat grows tedious. And we have ofttimes seen the delicate meats abandoned for the taste of the gross; and then the return afterward to the same again when the appetite has been satisfied of the other.

"But because, as we have said, it is not lawful even through any unjust occasion to desire what is another man's, we will leave the married to their husbands and take the others of which our city does set a copious number before our eyes. And in bestowing our love we would rather seek the widow than the rude maiden who, surely too stupid for such mystery, is only after the greatest effort made responsive to a man's desire. Such trouble is hardly if at all needed on the widow's account. Young maidens do love, to be sure, but they know not what it is they desire; and seldom can they follow with any attentive mind the dalliance of the lover as can the widows in whom antique fires suddenly take force. Awakening desires, which through long neglect have been forgot, come now to such fulfill-ment that they (too late!) beweep the lost times and long solitary nights passed alone in their widowish beds. And so it seems then, that these of any in whom rests the right to submit themselves to others, are rather the ones to be loved."

Then answered Feramonte: "Most excellent Queen, what you have said of the married, I had already determined in my mind that so it ought to be. Hearing now the same from you I am more than ever reassured of it. But, touching the maiden and the widow, setting the married apart for the reasons you have alleged, I am of the contrary opinion.

"It seems more reasonable that the maid rather than the widow ought to be desired, for is not the love of a virgin damsel more firm and assured than that of the widow? The widow has already loved one other time before. She has seen and felt many things of love and knows what shortcomings may follow in its wake. And therefore, knowing these things better than the maid, does she not love but fairly and without enthusiasm? Doubting and changeable, she desires now this and now that, and knows not whether, for her most delight and greatest honor, to bind herself or not. And sometimes she will neither the one nor the other, so that determination does waver in her mind and never is amorous passion allowed to lay hold of stability.

"But to the maid these things are altogether unknown. And therefore, as she persuades herself with good advisement that, of the many young men, she greatly pleases one, she then without further examination makes choice of him as her lover. And to him only she disposes her love, not knowing how to show any contrary act. Nor does she seek further concerning her love any new schemes for the more certain binding of her lover. Quickly and without complication she disposes her wounded heart at the will and pleasure of him who simply pleases her and serves him who is her only lord; something, as I have already said, that never happens with the widow. And therefore, is the other rather to be pursued.

"Furthermore, the maiden prolongs with more efficacy those very things that one of her sort has yet to see, hear, and experience; desiring to see, hear, and effect more than any who have already seen, heard, and experienced them. The truth in this is evident. Among the other occasions in which our life does delight and wish to ever extend is the constant revelation of new things such as we have never seen before. To see these newest of things we even take great pleasure in running with the liveliest possible pace toward that which above all other things we strive to flee, and that is death, the final end to all mortal life.

"The maid knows not that delightful conjunction by which we come into the world, and yet it is natural to every living creature to be drawn through desire thereunto. Further, so often has she heard from those who know what manner of thing it is, how much sweetness does consist in what words have fired with desire, she therefore comes naturally to it. Yearning to experience the thing of which she yet knows nothing she boldly moves with a kindled heart toward this concourse. And with whom is it presumed to be had but him only whom she has already made lord of her mind? This heat shall not be found in the widow, because having already experienced and felt what manner of thing it was, she is, in consequence, merely provoked by it all. So, then, the maid shall love more and be more diligent to the pleasure of her lover than the widow, through reasons already set down. To what end shall we then stay any further in asking that the maid ought not rather to be loved than the widow?"

"You reason well," said the queen, "and very well you defend your opinion. But still, we will show you with apparent proof how you as well ought to hold the same judgment as do we in this contention. But first you need look with a straight eye into the nature of love. Both in the maid as in the widow, and so in the widow as in the maid, we see Eros to be firm, strong, and constant. That this is true, Dido and Ariadne with their doings have left us an example. And if this young god is neither in one nor in the other, nothing of the aforesaid activity will therefore follow. So in this case it is convenient that each of them do love if we are to have any example of that about which both you and I have already talked. Therefore, in matters of love let us examine both maid and widow without looking into which of them is most discreetly enamored. As we are certain of the widow, we shall show you how much more diligent the widow is of her lover's pleasure than is the maid.

"Undoubtedly, among the things that a woman esteems more dearly above anything else is her virginity. And there is good reason, because therein consists all the honor of her subsequent life. Presumably she shall never be so completely urged forward to love, of which she shall not willingly approve except to aim only at the one to whom she is intended as wife through matrimonial law. And therefore, we go not about examining this, for unquestionably it is the case that he who would love in order to marry ought rather to love the maid than the widow. And if he loves her not and she knows of it, she shall be indifferent and slow in giving herself to him for that reason. Further, the virgin maiden is generally fearful and is not subtle enough to find ways and means by which she may safely take the stolen delights.

"But different is the widow who has already honorably lost that which the other is so slow in giving. And being without the same, in giving herself to another she may not at all be accused of its absence. Having no longer such a concern she becomes the more adventurous, because, as has been said, the chiefest occasion that stirs suspicion is not in her. Besides, she knows better the secret ways and so puts them in good use.

"What you have said of the maiden being desirous of a thing that she has not yet tried, and being made more diligent to this than the widow who already knows what manner a thing it is, is not at all so. The contrary is true. The chaste damsel does not at the first time in such pleasures run to any great joy, and it is more often noisome than pleasant to her. We say that delight and pleasure comes the more only after it is seen, heard, or felt, and the more inclined everyone is in following the same through experience. This thing, we reason, does not follow the order of many other things, which, once or twice being seen, are afterward no longer desired. But rather, the oftener it is put to good effect so much the more likely one covets its return with affection. He whom it pleases desires more than does he whom it ought to please though he has not as yet tasted of it.

"Forasmuch as the widow has the least to sacrifice and is the best able to give, she shall be more liberal and less reluctant than the maiden who must give the dearest thing she has. Also the widow shall be drawn to such attractions sooner than the maid. For which cause then, let the widow be loved rather than the maid."

THE TENTH QUESTION
proposed by Ascaleon

(A beautiful and noble lady beloved of all, but especially by two young knights, is falsely accused and condemned to the fire. If there is a knight who would fight in defense of her honor against the first who should hold to the contrary, and should overcome, she should be free; but if he should be beaten then she should burn. The two lovers come forward and fight, and one allows himself to be vanquished for her sake. Which of the two should she have loved the better?)

While thus regretting his misfortune he inwardly thought as well that if he, before any other, should go armed into the field saying the gentlewoman ought to die and allow himself to be overcome, he might by this device cause her to escape.

I T WAS APPROPRIATE THAT ASCALEON, WHO, IN THE CIRCLE, SAT NEXT to the duke Feramonte, should now propound, and accordingly he began his tale in this manner:

•

Most excellent Queen, I recall that in our city there once was a certain fair and noble gentlewoman. Of marvelous beauty, she had but recently been left widowed by a worthy husband and was since become most dearly admired by many young gentlemen.

Of that number there were two wellborn, courageous knights, each of whom did strive with all his will to attain her love. And while this continued, it happened by chance that certain members of her dead husband's family did bring an unjust accusation against her before the magistrate. By false evidence it was proved, and through this untrue process she was condemned to the fire.

But because the conscience of the judge was perplexed, seeming as it were to recognize the unjustness of the proof, he was willing to commit his life to the gods and Fortune's chance by tying a condition to his given sentence.

Proclaiming that when the time came for the gentlewoman to be led to the fire, if there could be found a knight who would combat in defense of her honor and overcome one who would maintain the contrary, she should then be free. But if the contrary should happen, she was to be burned according to the deemed sentence.

When the condition was understood by her two lovers, by chance sooner known to one than to the other, he who knew of it soonest at once took it upon his honor, mounted on horseback and came into the field to challenge any that would come maintaining the guilt of the gentlewoman.

The other, who knew of the sentence somewhat later than the

first, became very sorrowful on hearing how the knight was already to the field in her defense with no place left for another to act upon her behalf. He imagined that because of his slackness he had lost the love of his beloved lady and that the other was now justly deserved of the same. While thus regretting his misfortune he inwardly thought as well that if he before any other should go armed into the field saying the gentlewoman ought to die and allow himself to be overcome, he might by this device cause her to escape. Acting then according to this plan, he effected the gentlewoman's escape and she was forthwith delivered from peril.

After certain days had passed, the first knight went to her and recommended himself to her consideration. He reminded her how, to preserve her from death, he had offered himself to the same peril on that previous day and, thanks to the gods and to his own good force, had delivered both her and himself from so harsh a fate. If it would please her to accord him his just due he now lay claim to her love, which above all else he had always desired.

And afterward with like entreaties came the second knight, saying how, for her sake, he had hazarded his own life and allowed himself to be overcome so that she should not burn. The very act of which had purchased for him eternal infamy instead of an honorable victory, which certainly would have been his had he not cared so well for her security and been willing to use his full force.

The gentlewoman thanked each of them most benignly and promised both due recompense for the services she had received from them. And then when they had departed from her she found herself in great uncertainty. To which of them should she now give her love; to the first or to the second? And upon which of them, I now pray counsel of you, would you say that she ought sooner bestow the same?

•

"We deem," said the queen, "that the first is to be loved and the last to be left. The first, forceful and assured, showed his love in a forthright fashion by giving himself to every peril that might happen through the future battle. Death itself might very well have followed in the defense of her, if such a battle to be done against him had been as lawful to any of the enemies of the gentlewoman as it was to the lover. Nor was it ever evident that one should come against him who would allow himself to be overcome, as eventually happened.

"The last truly went well-advised that he would not die and knew by his own action that the woman as well would not die. Then, forasmuch as he put least in the adventure, he merits to gain the less. Let the first as the just deserver of his action have the fair gentlewoman for his beloved."

Ascaleon said: "O most prudent Queen, what are you saying? Does not one reward suffice for welldoing without craving further due? Truly yes. The first is well-requited by the honor he has had from all for the received victory. And what greater reward needs he than honor, the reward of virtue? The received honor was more than ample for a greater deed than he did. And he that with all his wit came well-advised, ought he go unrecompensed? And is he to be evilly spoken of as well by everyone, having no less than the first helped the gentlewoman to escape? Is not the wit to foresee every man's force? How so, if this man with all his wit came forward in defense of the gentlewoman, ought he for his desert be rejected? God forbid it should be so.

"If he knew not of her difficulty so soon as the other this was not through negligence. Perhaps had he known of it before the other he would have done the same, believing this to be the proper action. And believing this, the reward justly ought to follow. And if the gentlewoman rightly sees to him, her love will be that reward. And yet you say the contrary."

"God defend you from your opinion," answered the queen, "that vice coming to a good end merits the same reward as virtue with the like ending. Rather, if vice deserves correction, then no worldly reward can justly satisfy virtue. Although we cannot prove it with any certainty, who shall deny us believing that the knight, envious of the good turn he saw prepared for the other, was moved to such an enterprise only to disturb the same and not for the love he claimed for the gentlewoman. And even should his scheme fail, he is a fool who under the guise of an enemy expects compensation for helping another.

"Infinite are the ways by which it is possible to show at once with open friendship the love that we can bear another without showing ourselves as enemies, and then with colored words make much of the profit in it. All this that we have said may not suffice as answer enough for you, in whom old age more than anything else ought to have made wise; but we believe when your mind shall have truly digested these things you shall not find our judgment guileful but true, and to be followed."

And so she held her peace.

THE ELEVENTH QUESTION
proposed by a Gentlewoman named Graziosa

*(Which is of greater delight to the lover:
to see his mistress present, or not seeing her, to think lovingly of her?)*

And many, not being able to move, stand like posts while others tangling and cross-ing their legs fall helplessly to the ground. And there are some who lose their speech.

*t*HERE FOLLOWED AFTER HIM A GENTLEWOMAN OF MILD DISPOSI-
tion whose name was Graziosa; and assuredly such a
name was in harmony with her nature, for when she
began to speak, the words came both modest and humble
to the ear. "The time is come, O most virtuous Queen, for me to
propound in my turn a question. So that the approaching hour
before our last feasting be spent only in talk, I shall briefly set forth
what willingly I would rather pass over. And without going beyond
the limits of deference to yourself or the order of the rest I shall
question you this: Which is of greater delight to the lover: to see his
love beside him, or being absent, to think amorously of her?"

"My gracious Graziosa," replied the queen, "we do believe that
much greater delight is to be taken in the thinking than in the
beholding. For all the senses do then graciously feel a marvelous joy
in the contemplation of the thing loved and, as it were, do satisfy
inflamed desires in the pleasure of the thought alone. Whereas it
happens not in the beholding, for only the visible sense feels joy,
and the others then kindled with such a desire are not able to endure
it and so remain subdued. And too, that visible spirit sometimes
demands so much of his desire that of necessity he is constrained to
withdraw himself, remaining of small account and altogether vanquished. So we do conclude from all this that greater delight is in
the thinking thereof than in the beholding of it."

"That thing which is loved," answered the gentlewoman, "the
more it is seen so much more does it give pleasure. And therefore,
I believe a thing beheld brings greater delight than the reflection on
it. But because even beauty at first gives pleasure on sight, so then
through continued regard such delight is multiplied in the mind
until Love himself is engendered with all the pleasures that spring

from him. No beauty is so much loved than when it pleases the eye and contents the same. Therefore, in seeing they are contented, and in imagining their desire is increased. He that is contented feels more delight than does he who desires to content himself.

"We may see and know by Laodamia[39] how much more the present sight than the absent thought does delight. We are to believe that her Protesilaus never departed from her thought. Nevertheless, was she ever seen disposed to other than melancholy, refusing as well to deck and apparel herself with costly garments? This never happened when she saw him. For whenever she was in his presence she was merry and gracious, always joyful and trimly attired. What more evident testimony will we have than this, that gladness is greater in the sight than in the thought? It is in outward doings, which in the heart are hidden, that such things may be comprehended."

To this the queen then gave answer: "Things both delightful and noisome that approach most near the mind, bring more annoyance and joy than do those things that are far off from the same. And who doubts that the thought abides in the mind and that the mind is not from the eye?

"Through the particular virtue of the mind they have their sight, and it is convenient for them by various means to render their propositions to the animated understanding. Having then in mind a sweet thought of the loved, perhaps some act to bring together both lover and beloved, it becomes more real than imagined. It is then he sees the same with those eyes to which nothing, no, not even long distance, may be hidden. Then he speaks with her whom he loves and perhaps with a piteous style tells of the vexations sustained for her sake. Then is it lawful for him to take her in his arms without fear and do with her according to his desire. Marvelously happy is he now with her, holding her wholly at his pleasure. Now if he were truly in her presence nothing of this sort would happen, because the sight of her alone is pleasing enough without passing further.

"And, as we say, love is timorous and fearful. In beholding, it does make the heart tremble in such a way as to leave neither thought nor spirit in its place. For many, with the prolonged beholding of their ladies are lost those natural attractions, and they remain vanquished. And many, not being able to move, stand like posts while others tangling and crossing their legs fall helplessly to the ground. And there are some who lose their speech. And by sight we can count many others to whom like things have happened. All of which would have been more acceptable to them had they not happened at all. How then can one find delight in what should willingly be fled? We confess that if it were possible to see without fear it should be a great delight, but then without imagination little or nothing in the absence of bodily sight pleases very much.

"And should what we have spoken of come to pass through the thought, it is obvious to the senses as well, yes, and much more. For we do find that men with imagination have gone beyond the heavens and have tasted of eternal peace. So, more delights the thought than the sight.

"And if you say that Laodamia was melancholy in her thoughts, we do not deny it. It was a dolorous rather than an amorous thought that did trouble her. She, to her own harm as it were, given to portents, always doubted the death of Protesilaus and continued to believe him well. Because of this disbelief, thoughts contrary to those of which we speak could never enter her. But rather, sorrowing through this occasion she had cause enough to show a troublesome and heavy look."

THE TWELFTH QUESTION
proposed by Parmenio

(A young gentleman in love with a young maiden resorts to a wrinkled and hideous old hag as go-between. She contrives a meeting between them. However, during the attempted assignation all are taken together in surprise by the brothers of the young woman and the unlucky suitor is condemned by the brothers to lie both with their sister and the old beggar woman, each for a year, and to have converse precisely alike with each. Only, he may choose which he will take first and which last. Of the two, which should he have taken for the first year?)

You
are in our hands, discovered in an attempt to dishonor us, and for this we may punish you
if we wish. Instead, we give you a choice of one or the other of these two ways.

P ARMENIO, FOR IT WAS HE WHO SAT NEXT TO THE GENTLEWOMAN Graziosa, seeing that the queen had finished, began to speak without further ado:

•

Most mighty Queen, I was for many years companion of a young gentleman, to whom happened what I now intend to show. As much as any man could ever love a woman, he loved a fair young damsel of our city, gracious, gentle, and very rich, both of family and possessions. And for all that I could gather from it, being confidant and privy to this love tale, she loved him as well.

But fearing it should become public knowledge and that he would not again be able to speak with her, the gentleman concealed his love from all but his own secret heart. Until the time that he might safely reveal his intent and be assured in like manner of hers, he trusted no one who should attempt to speak of the matter.

Still, compelled in his desire, since he could not disclose himself to her, he resolved by some other person to make her aware of all that he suffered on her account. And thinking to himself for many days by whom he might most safely communicate his intent to her, he saw one day an old beggar woman enter the house of his beloved to ask her alms. Leaving from the same door, she was observed more carefully by the young gentleman as she went her way. Hideous and wrinkled, of tawny and jaundiced color, she was so despiteful to behold as to be unlike any he had ever seen before. Many times he saw her return in this same manner, and for the like occasion. And soon his heart gave him to rest his entire trust in her, telling him that through her alone he might fully accomplish his desire without arousing the least suspicion. Calling her to him he promised her great gifts if she would help him in what he should demand of her.

And when she swore to do all in her power for him, the gentleman revealed then his mind and made her privy to his amorous desire.

The old hag went at once to the young gentlewoman and informed her of the love my friend did bear her; and in certifying to the damsel his lacklove case she discovered likewise that the young woman did love him above all other things in this world. A scheme was devised on the spot by which the young man should secretly attend his beloved's desires. And presently, as she had appointed, he found himself following her to the house of the gentlewoman.

No sooner were they entered therein, than through a misfortune, the young woman, the old hag, and the young man were all three discovered and taken together in surprise by the brothers of the young maiden. The truth of what they did there was forced out, and in time they confessed the whole matter for what it was. But because the lady's brothers were friends of the gentleman as well; and knowing that he had as yet attained nothing that might redound to their shame, they intended him no harm, as they might well have in such a case. Laughing, they spoke to him in this manner:

"You are in our hands, discovered in an attempt to dishonor us, and for this we may punish you if we wish. Instead, we give you choice of one or the other of these two ways. If we spare your life you must choose to lie with this old harridan and with our sister, each for one year. But you will swear faithfully that should you take upon yourself to lie with each of them a year and the young woman be your first choice, as many times you kiss and have done with her so shall you kiss and have do with the old woman the second year. And should you take instead the old hag for the first, look how many times you shall kiss and touch her, for likewise must you do the same, no more and no less, to the young woman in the second year."

The young man, having heard his sentence and desirous indeed of continuing this life, answered that he would lie as required with these two for the two years. And so his choice was granted to him. But now in great doubt was he with which of them he should first begin, the one or the other?

•

"Dear Fiammetta, for his greater consolation, which of them would you counsel he should first choose to begin his sentence?"

Fiammetta and likewise the whole company smiled in bemusement at this unlikely tale as she made ready to answer:

"According to our judgment, the young gentleman ought rather to take the fair young woman than the foul old hag, because no present good action ought to be left for the future. Nor is the evil to be taken in anticipation of future rewards, for even we know how uncertain are things to come. And in doing the contrary of what I tell of, many have already regretted too late. And if any have praised himself for doing so, not duty but Fortune has therein helped him. Let the fair therefore be taken first."

"You make me marvel greatly," said Parmenio, "in your belief that the present good ought not to be left for the future. To what end then is it convenient for us to follow and bear with a valiant mind our worldly troubles when we may flee them, if it were not through the future eternal kingdoms promised to us by hope? It is a marvelous thing that such a shock of people as are in the world, all laboring to the end that in time they may partake of their reward, should remain so long in error. To enjoy first the good before the trouble is to say that later trouble were better than present good.

"It seems to me a thing very just that after all affliction one may expect rest. To desire first the good without the trouble in my

judgment ought not to be. Neither can it bring delight. Who then
will give counsel to anyone that he lie first with a fair gentlewoman
one year (which is surely the only reward and joy of him that must
lie with her) when next must follow the vexation and unpleasant life
of doing in every same act with a loathsome old woman what he
enjoyed with the young woman?

"Nothing is so spoiling to a delightful life as to remember that
after death we shall be found spotted. This death, returning to our
memory as an enemy inconsistent to our being, does deprive us of
all goodness and pleasure. And while it is remembered, there can
never be joy tasted in worldly things. Likewise, no delight can be
had with the young woman that is not troubled or destroyed in
thinking and remembering that it behooves him to do as much with
a most vile old crone who shall always remain before the eyes of his
mind. Time that flies with an inestimable wing shall seem to him
to overfly, lessening each day a great quantity of the owing hours
so that the joy in it is not tasted. Whereas infallible future sorrow
is tarried for.

"From this I would judge that the contrary would be the better
counsel. That is, all trouble from which gracious rest is hoped is
more delightful than the joy after which vexation awaits. For Leander, the cold waters seemed warm, the dreadful time of the dark
night appeared clear as the perfect day, and turmoils stilled each
time he went to his Hero. With all the strength of his arms he swam
through the salt surges between Sestus and Abydos, delayed only
in his coming by the pleasure he imagined to have of her. God
forbid, then, that a man should covet rest before excessive labor, or
reward before doing his service, or delight before he has tasted of
tribulation. For should even that way be taken, as we have already
said, the future discomfort would so much hinder the immediate joy

that no joy at all but rather vexation would be the only result.

"What delight could the delicate meats, the instruments sounded with cunning hand, and other marvelous joys made for Dionysius the Tyrant[40] bring to Damocles once he knew of the sharp-pointed sword suspended by a fine thread over his head?

"Let then sorrowful occasions be first encountered, and afterward with pleasure, and that without suspicion, gracious delights will surely follow."

The queen made him answer, saying: "You answer in part as though we did reason of eternal joys. For the purchase of such, there is no doubt but that all troubles ought to be taken in hand and all worldly wealth with its pleasures be left apart. But in this instance we speak not of them, but discuss instead a question of worldly delights and worldly discomfits. Upon this we answer. As we have said before, take rather every worldly delight followed by worldly effort than any worldly effort that puts off worldly delight. For he that has time and delays time, loses time. Fortune grants her goodness with various mutations, which is better taken when given than struggled for in great turmoil. If her wheel stood firm and stable while a man toiled so much that he need toil no more, we would then say that it were better to take the pain first. But who is certain that after the evil worse may not follow instead of the better that is hoped for? The times, together with worldly things, are all transitory. It could well happen that in taking first the old woman, the young gentlewoman may die before the year (which shall never seem to wax less) is out. Or her brothers may repent themselves of what they have done. Or then again, she may be given to some other or perhaps stolen away, so that after one evil there shall follow a worse to the taker.

"But contrariwise, if the young woman is chosen first the taker could thereby have his desire as long as he wishes. For need the vexatious thoughts follow that you say must follow because of this? That we must all die is certain. And to lie with an old woman is a misfortune that can be avoided by any clever man capable of the many remedies now at hand. Worldly things are to be taken by the discreet with this condition: that each one while he holds and enjoys them shall also dispose himself with a generous mind to restore or leave them when that time comes.

"He that busies himself so that in the end he may rest is a true example of one who cannot have rest without drudging for it. And since he therefore assumes troubles so that in the end he may rest, how much more is it to be presumed that if rest were as available as trouble he would sooner take that than this? Nor must one believe that Leander, if he had been able to have Hero without crossing the tempestuous arm of the sea (in which he eventually perished) would not rather have taken her than swum the same. It is indeed convenient to take Fortune's chances at the time she gives them.

"No gift is so small that it is not better than one promising to be greater. And as for future things, let remedies be taken and the present be governed according to their qualities. It is a natural thing to prefer good over evil when they concur equally; and he that desires the contrary follows not natural reason but his own folly. We confess that after troubles, quietness is more gracious and better known than before, but not that quietness is to be taken in preference to the other.

"It is possible for wise men and fools to use the counsels both of fools and of wise men according to their liking. But for all that, the infallible verity is not altered, which gives us leave to see in this situation that he to whom was given such a choice is to take rather the fair young woman than the loathsome hag."

THE THIRTEENTH QUESTION
proposed by Massalino

(Which was the greater: the good fortune and happiness of the husband who got again the lost wife whom he thought dead, or the loyalty of the lover who brought her out alive from her tomb and touched her not in restoring her to her husband?)

But such is it now come to pass that what love would
not vouchsafe to grant me in her lifetime, cannot be denied me now that she is dead.
Assuredly, if I die for it, I will kiss the face of her in death that living I loved so well.

ᴍASSALINO, WHO SAT ON THE RIGHT HAND OF THE QUEEN and next to Parmenio completing the circle, now spoke up in this manner: "It is fitting that I lastly do now propound my question. And to the end that I may make the pleasantly told tales and the previous propounded questions seem more sweet, I therefore tell you a short tale worth the hearing wherein there falls a question that quite properly will make an end withal."

•

I have at one time heard say that there was in our city of Parthenope a very rich gentleman who had for a wife an exceedingly fair young gentlewoman. It was she whom he loved above all worldly things. Now at the same time, this gentlewoman was entirely beloved of a knight from the same city. But she loved him not, nor did she care for him at all. And because of this, the knight was never able to get from her either good words or courteous countenance.

While he thus lived comfortless of such love, it happened that he was called to the regiment of a city not so far distant from this port. And accordingly, he went there and governed the same for the full time of his residence in that place.

During the period of his service, there came to him a messenger who, after other news, said:

Sir, you shall understand that the gentlewoman of our city whom you loved so entirely above all others, this morning laboring with great grief to be delivered of child, died not being delivered, and was in my presence and that of her family honorably set to rest in the place of her ancestors.

The knight gave ear to this news with a heavy heart, and not

without great sorrow endured the telling of it. He showed no alteration of countenance whatever, but to himself he said thus: Hah!
Wretched Death, cursèd be thy power! Thou hast deprived me of
her whom I loved to distraction, and whom I desired more to serve
than any other worldly creature. But such is it now come to pass
that what Love would not vouchsafe to grant me in her lifetime,
cannot be denied me now that she is dead. Assuredly, if I die for it,
I will kiss the face of her in death that living I loved so well.

And staying upon this determination, he waited until it was
night, and taking with him the messenger whom he then best
trusted he traveled the dreadful dark ways until at last he came to
the city. Having entered the same, he went at once to that sepulchre
in which the body of the gentlewoman lay buried. And, after he had
comforted his companion that he should attend him there without
fear, he opened the sepulchre and entered therein, lamenting all the
while with piteous plaints. He kissed the gentlewoman and took her
into his arms. Then, not satisfied with this, he began to feel her here
and there and to put his hand into her frozen bosom between her
two cold breasts. But soon becoming more bold than was proper,
he began to seek out under the rich attire that covered her, going
and feeling with a fearful hand hither and thither the secret parts
of her body till at last he spread the hand upon her stomach. And
here he thought suddenly to feel the weak pulses move with the
faintest of action.

At this he became very fearful, but yet his love making him
bolder, he tried further with a more assured attention and knew
suddenly that she was not dead. At once and first of all he drew her
out of that place with a sweet tenderness, and then wrapping her
in a great mantle (leaving the sepulchre gates ajar) he and his servant

carried her secretly to the house of his mother. Here, he conjured his mother through the power of God that she should reveal neither this nor anything else to any living person; and then caused great fires to be made so that the cold members would now be comforted. But because the lost forces did not soon return, in due order it was urgently willed by one perhaps skilled in such cases that there be prepared a hot room. In this were first strewn various potent herbs, and after, as was proper for one in such a plight, the gentlewoman was herein placed and tenderly and gently settled. And soon in this hot room where she continued for a time, the blood that was congealed about the heart began from the received heat to disperse throughout the cold veins; and the breath of life once more began its course in the half-dead woman. Slowly responding in consequence, she called out to her mother, and then in time, asked where she was.

The knight, answering her in place of her mother, gave her to understand she was in a safe place, and that she should now comfort herself. This she did do, resting awhile in a quiet manner, but suddenly she called out for the help of her woman Lucina. And therewith, as it pleased the gods, she was, with trouble and peril, above all expectation, delivered of a fair son. Now disburdened and joyful in the new child, she was provided nurses both for the charge of herself and also of her son.

Now, after all these heavy troubles, the gentlewoman with her son newly born to the world was well returned to perfect understanding before she saw either the knight who loved her or his mother who was pressed to do her service. Neither did she see any of her family or kinfolks about her or caring for her. And this set her mind in thoughtful perplexity, as it were. Greatly bewildered, she spoke out: "Where am I? What wonder is this? Who has brought me here to this place wherein I never was before?"

And the knight, now coming to her, answered: "Gentlewoman, wonder not and comfort yourself, for what you see has been the pleasure of the gods, and I shall tell you how this has come to pass." Then, declaring from the beginning to the end all that had happened to her, he concluded that through him she and her son were alive; by which he now reasoned to her that they were forever bound to be at his pleasure.

The gentlewoman agreed that this must be so. And knowing full well that she could not by any other means but only by those as he showed her have come into the hands of this knight, she did with a devout voice first offer up thanks to the immortal gods, and after, did thank him, offering herself always to be at his pleasure and service.

The knight then replied, saying: "Gentlewoman, since you know yourself to be beholden to me, I wish, in requital of my welldoing, that you comfort yourself here in this house until I return from my post, to which it is now so long since I was appointed that the duration of it is almost at an end. And you shall promise me faithfully that in no way will you reveal yourself without my license, either to your husband or to any other person."

The gentlewoman answered him that she was unable to deny him either this or any other request, and that assuredly, she would accommodate herself to what was to be. By her oath made to him, she affirmed never to cause herself to be known without his pleasure.

The knight now remained in her service two further days. And seeing the gentlewoman out of all peril and now well cared for he recommended her and the child to his mother's charge, and so departed.

He returned to the government of his said office, which in a little while was honorably discharged, and soon again he was home to his house and possessions, and to the gentlewoman by whom he was graciously received.

Certain days after his return he prepared a great banquet to which he now invited the husband of the gentlewoman, her brothers, and many others who were friends of them all. And the bidden guests being set down at table, the gentlewoman, according to the pleasure of the knight, came appareled in the garments in which she was buried, decked with the crown, rings, and other precious ornaments as was the custom then. And, as instructed that morning by the knight, she placed herself next to her husband, with the knight seated on her other side where she fed without uttering any word at all.

This gentlewoman was many times observed by her husband. And because of her attire and also her ornaments, it seemed to him that he recognized her to be his wife, and the garments to be those in which she was buried. Yet for that, he dared not once give her a word, knowing that he had buried his wife dead in her sepulchre, and in no way could he believe her to be risen again. He believed rather that she was some other who did resemble his lost wife, imagining that it was easier to find one woman in attire and ornaments like another than to raise up a dead body.

But still, for all this, he turned many times toward the knight, and in the end asked him who she was. "Ask of her," answered the knight, "who she is, for I cannot tell, out of so unpleasant a place have I brought her."

Then the husband asked of the gentlewoman who she was. And she answered him:

"By this knight, in ways unknown to me, I was brought to this place and returned to the gracious life that is by everyone desired."

When these words were heard there wanted no amazement in the husband that did not further increase. And so it remained until the banquet was ended. At which time the knight then led the husband of the gentlewoman into a private chamber. And with him went the gentlewoman and the others likewise that banqueted with them. Here they found the gentlewoman's comely and pleasing son in the nurse's arms, who was then delivered by the knight into the father's hands with these words: "This is your son."

And then giving him the right hand of his wife, he said: "This is your wife, the mother of this child."

He then showed him and the others how it came about that she was brought to his house. There was much wonder at the story as it was told, and also great joy. But more so than any other did the husband find joy in his wife, and the wife with her husband in their child.

And, after thanking the knight, both of them with the child returned in happiness to their own house which rang full of marvelous joy for many days thereafter.

In his dealing with the gentlewoman the knight did in all ways treat her with a tenderness and pure faith that was as if she had been his sister. And now the question is propounded. Which of these two was the greater, the loyalty of the knight or the joy of the husband who had now gotten again his lost wife whom he supposed dead? I pray you to say your opinion and what you would judge of it.

•

"In our opinion," answered the queen, "great was the joy in the recovered wife and her child. But likewise, noble and very great was the devotion of the knight. Altogether, it is a natural thing to be glad of getting again things that are lost. Nor could it, as it would to any other, be otherwise. Especially in the recovery of a thing so greatly loved before. And with a child, there could hardly be made so great a joy ever.

"Yet, we do not claim for it more importance than what a man of proper virtue is constrained to do in being loyal. For being loyal or not being loyal can be a choice. Either thing is possible. We say that he who is loyal to one so greatly loved does a great and noble thing in keeping loyalty. And in him, loyalty does increase in far greater quantity than does joy in the other. And this we do so judge."

"Truly," said Massalino, "I believe, most renowned Queen, it is as you say. Still, it seems to me a great matter to think about. With so great a joy as was in him that had gotten again his wife, a comparison of greatness could be made in another thing. Is it any different a thing than the great grief that cannot be supported except only when through death it is lost? Furthermore, if the knight were faithful, as it is already said, did he not do only what was his duty? Are we not all bound to the working of virtue? He that does only what he is duty bound to do does well, yet it is not to be considered so great a matter. Therefore, I imagine that joy rather than loyalty may be judged the greater."

"You with your words," returned the queen, "do contradict yourself. Man ought easily as well rejoice in the goodness of God in taking him away as in a working of virtue. If the one could be in the one case as sorrowful as the other could be in the other case disloyal, why then, I might agree to your judgment. To follow the laws of nature when they cannot be fled is of no matter. But to obey the positive laws is a virtue of the mind. And the virtues of the mind are to be preferred both for greatness as well as for every other respect before the natural inclinations. And if virtuous works (making due recompense) surmount all other workings in greatness, it may be said that having been loyal endures always for its own sake. Joy may be turned into sudden sorrow, or else in a short space of time become little or nothing when the thing that has made one happy is lost. And therefore let it be said, of him that uprightly will judge, the loyalty of the knight is rather to be preferred than the joy of the other."

fOLLOWING MASSALINO THERE WERE NO OTHERS WHO HAD ANY-
thing more to say, for they all had now propounded their
questions. The sun so nearly set had left the place replete
with a temperate air. And for these reasons then, Fiammetta, most
reverent Queen of this amorous people, raising her foot, said: "Gentlemen and Gentlewomen, your questions are finished. To these

(the gods be thanked) we have, according to our small knowledge in following pleasant reasoning rather than matter of contention, made answer. That much more might well have been addressed, the same we know, yes, and in far better sort than we have done. But what we have said must suffice our pastime, and for the rest, let it remain to the philosophers of Athens.

"We see Phoebus low enough that he now shines over us with a glancing ray. And with the air refreshed we note that our feast, which in coming here we left in excessive heat, is once more attended by our companions. It would seem well, therefore, that we return to the same."

This being said, Fiammetta, with delicate hand took from her head the laurel crown and in the place where she had sat laid it down, saying further: "Until such time as we shall return for a like discussion I leave here this crown of my honor and of yours."

And having said this, hand in hand with Filocolo now risen with the rest she directed them from their little meadow and so returned them all to their feasting. From every side was heard once more the pleasant sounds of instruments, with the air resounding sweetly of amorous songs. And for the rest of the day no part of the garden was without banqueting; even to the last hour they all continued merrily.

But night being come upon them with its stars showing forth their light, it seemed proper to the lady and to them all that they should depart and return to the city. Entering therein Filocolo took his leave of Fiammetta and said to her: "Most noble Fiammetta, if the gods should ever grant me that I were again my own as I am now another's, without doubt I should be presently yours. But because mine own I am not, I cannot give myself to another. Howbeit for so much as this miserable heart can receive strange fire, so much more does it feel a rekindling through your inestimable worthiness. And so it shall feel always, and incessantly with more effect shall it desire never to be forgetful of your worthiness."

With much feeling Fiammetta thanked Filocolo for these courteous words, and as he departed she added that it would surely please the gods if a gracious peace be quickly brought to his desire.

NOTES

1. FLORIO, so called FILOCOLO: The adventures of Florio in Boccaccio's *Filocolo* are so melodramatic and complex even a brief synopsis risks reading as a parody. They begin before his birth with a pledge made in Rome by a certain Lelius that, should a child be granted him in his barren marriage with Giulia, a holy pilgrimage to the tomb of the apostle Saint James in Spain would be made. Overjoyed by the miraculous news that his wife is now indeed pregnant, Lelius and Giulia set off with a large company of pilgrims and proceed to Santiago de Compostela in fulfillment of his vow.

The Devil is angered by this forthcoming honor to Saint James, and appearing before King Felice in Seville, he informs him falsely that his country is under attack by the Romans. To protect his kingdom and repel the invaders, Felice and his forces fall upon the company of Lelius believing them to be the enemy. In the ensuing battle Lelius is killed, and the king, discovering his error too late, returns home bringing Giulia to his court where she is received and treated kindly by the queen. However, she does not long outlive the death of Lelius, for soon, in giving birth to a girl-child she dies, by great coincidence, on the very day a son is born to the queen.

Brought up together as brother and sister, Florio and Biancofiore discover their mutual love. The king and queen oppose the romance, of course, and send Florio away in an effort to make him forget Biancofiore. This he cannot do, so the king, in his determination to separate them once and for all, falsely accuses Biancofiore of plotting to poison him. She is condemned to the stake, from which she is rescued in great style by her equally determined lover. Things go along in this way, with many dreadful adventures befalling the young lovers, until Felice, losing all patience, sells Biancofiore in slavery to certain traveling infidel merchants from Alexandria.

Florio sets out with his old and faithful tutor Ascaleon and others, in search of her. Concealing his name and station he calls himself Filocolo, the Love Weary, or, as Boccaccio intended by his uncertain Greek, the Pilgrim of Love.

It is in the early part of this search that Florio is driven by storm to take refuge in the harbor of Parthenope, and it is here awaiting repairs to his ship that he comes upon the garden where Fiammetta and her lover Galeone with their friends have gathered to while away the hot afternoon. The stories they tell each other are those that are set down in this book, the *Thirteen Questions of Love*.

Many more adventures, rescues, and escapes take place before the faithful lovers are finally united in true love and a happy afterlife, but these do not concern us here. The immortality of Boccaccio's genius is concentrated in this small section of Florio's meeting with Fiammetta and the consequent telling of these thirteen tales.

2. PARTHENOPE: This was the ancient name for the site of Naples. Here, according to legend, the body of the drowned sea nymph Parthenope was washed ashore by the sorrowing waves. A tomb for her was erected on this spot where later the city called Parthenope was built to her memory.

Orpheus was her downfall. As one of the treacherous Sirens, her reputation was not unknown to him. When Ulysses' ship, the *Argo*, sailed near the rocky abode of the Sirens, Orpheus tuned his lyre and began to sing to his fellow Argonauts, rendering harmless by his persuasive voice the fatal lure of the Sirens' songs. Seeing her intended victims sail safely past, Parthenope, in vexation, threw herself into the sea. Her sister sea-nymphs, now powerless to do further harm, were changed into rocks. In those days a very small margin for failure was tolerated in the camps of the gods.

3. PHEBEA and NOTUS: Phebea is a variation for Phoebe, another name for Diana the Moon goddess. It is also, by metonymy, the Moon itself. Notus was the South Wind, bringer of rain.

4. MARO: Publius Vergilius Maro was born in northern Italy near Mantua, October 15, in 70 B.C. Called Virgil, he was the greatest poet of the Augustan Age. He died returning from Athens in the company of the Emperor Augustus on September 21, in 19 B.C. and was buried in Naples, where his tomb was long a place of religious

pilgrimage. His most enduring works were the *Eclogues*, the *Georgics*, and the *Aeneid*.

5. GALEONE and FIAMMETTA: The great love of Boccaccio's life was Maria d'Aquino, the natural daughter of Robert king of Naples, and it was under her influence that Boccaccio became the great imaginative artist that he was. In his writings she is immortalized as Fiammetta; and Galeone, the ideal lover, is the counterpart of himself. In the Seventh Question, propounded by Galeone, the whole story of the love conflict that beset the liaison of Giovanni and Maria is recorded. What starts as a paean of poetic love to the beauty of Fiammetta in the recitative and ballad by Galeone, turns suddenly bitter by the arguments advanced by Fiammetta. In the harshest indictment possible, Fiammetta attacks with cynical cruelty all that Galeone lives for in his love of Fiammetta. It may be observed that in both the First Question, delivered by Florio, and the Seventh Question of Galeone's, Fiammetta does not allow rebuttal but has herself give the last word. Her loss of composure in each question is very apparent.

6. MARSYAS: Marsyas, a satyr of Phrygia, found the discarded flute of Minerva. He blew upon it, and drawing from it such ravishing sounds he was soon ill-advisedly tempted to challenge Apollo to a musical tournament. The god punished this presumptuous effrontery by flaying him alive. That Marsyas' hubris should have merited such excessive punishment shows how typically heartless was the justice of the Greek gods.

7. DIDO and AENEAS: Aeneas' escape from the Greeks after the fall of Troy begins all the adventures related by Virgil in the *Aeneid*.

At one point in this great epic poem, Aeneas and his Trojan companions are driven off course by a fierce sea storm toward the coast of Africa. Here they are warmly welcomed by Dido, queen of Carthage, who almost at once conceives an ardent passion for their leader Aeneas. He, for his part, indifferently willing but happy to terminate his wanderings, settles down to share the good life with her. However, Jupiter, involved as usual in the affairs of men, becomes impatient with the lack of excitement, and recalling to Aeneas his sense of duty commands him to resume his voyage. Dido, abandoned by Aeneas, in despair prepares for herself a high funeral pyre, the top of which she then mounts to be consumed in its flames. And Aeneas, far out at sea, seeing from the deck of his ship the smoke over Carthage, has an uneasy premonition that this part of his life is now finished forever.

8. PARIS and HELEN and MENELAUS: Paris, the shepherd son of Priam, king of Troy, was the seducer of Helen, wife of Menelaus, king of Sparta. Through the connivance of Venus, it was his unlawful liaison with Helen that set off the ten-year war that ultimately destroyed Troy. Paris was no great help to his father. And even his brother Hector said of him: "Evil Paris, beautiful, womancrazy, cajoling, better had you never been born, or killed or unwedded."

9. FABRITIUS and POMPEY: Gaius Fabritius, who lived in the third century B.C., was renowned for his incorruptibility. After the defeat of the Romans by Pyrrhus, king of Epirus, at Heraclea in 280 B.C. he was sent to negotiate the ransom and exchange of prisoners. His incorruptibility so impressed Pyrrhus that all the Roman prisoners were released to Fabritius without ransom. He is said to have died poor, and was regarded as an example of the early Roman

virtues. Pompey, on the other hand, was a commander of equivocal reputation. Ambition led him into quarrels with the senate, which led to the establishment of the First Triumvirate in 60 B.C. with Caesar, Crassus, and Pompey becoming rulers of Rome. He was never popular, and in Caesar's absence lost his hold on the populace. As a statesman he showed himself weak and irresolute.

10. MEDEA and JASON: Medea was notorious for her supernatural powers. When Jason appeared at the Colchian court of her father questing for the Golden Fleece, she conceived on sight a burning, immediate passion for the stranger, and put all her powers at his disposal without question. Needless to say he performed the demanded three dangerous tasks with precision, and won for himself his objective. Jason, bearing away the famous Fleece as well as the infatuated Medea, returned home to Iolchos to find his aged father Aeson at the point of death. Begging Medea to use her magic arts, he offered a portion of his own years so that they could be added to the age of his beloved father. But this Medea refused to accept, preferring Jason as he was. And, perhaps not caring for the prospect of the life of a young wife in the company of an aging husband, by incantation and spell she restored Aeson to what he was forty years before without penalty to Jason. Bored eventually by Medea's witchery, Jason abandoned her for others. It is the incanted spell and recipe for the magic brew of Medea that Boccaccio borrowed almost word for word from the Seventh Book of Ovid's *Metamorphoses,* using it in the Fourth Question, as described on page 49.

11. TANTALUS: Punished for some atrocious sin not recorded, Tantalus was made to stand deep in Hell to the level of his chin in a pool of water. And when with unbearable thirst he attempted to drink by bowing his head, the water would recede from his lips. Above his head were apple-laden trees that would sweep beyond his reach in the wind each time he moved to appease his continuous and insupportable hunger.

12. PENELOPE: Wife of Ulysses. Impatiently importuned by rude suitors to choose one among them during the absence of Ulysses, Penelope contrived to delay her decision until the weaving of a funeral pall for Laertes, her father-in-law, should be completed. What was woven during the day she secretly unravelled each night. In the meantime, waiting for the mantle to be finished, her suitors lazily sat around eating up the house and demanding of her a decision, while she, poor thing, with hope and Ulysses in her heart, put them off with this rather pathetic deception while anxiously awaiting her husband's homecoming.

13. HECTOR: The other son of Priam, Hector, was his pride as well as being the bravest of the Trojan warriors. It was he that felled Protesilaus, the first victim of the Trojan War.

14. DEIANIRA and HERCULES: Deianira, sometimes called Calydonis, was the wife of Hercules. Fording a storm-swollen stream one day, Hercules, so that he could overcome the waters alone, entrusted Deianira to the care of the centaur Nessus, who immediately attempted to make off with her. Enraged by this act, Hercules shot the fleeing Nessus in the back with an arrow envenomed with the poison of the Lernaean hydra, which is another story. Swearing revenge, the dying Nessus gave to Deianira his poisoned, blood-soaked tunic, telling her of its supposed potency for the reviving of a waning love. Years later when a false rumor came to Deianira that Hercules was enamored of Iole, she remembered the tunic and sent it to Hercules to restore his faltering love for her. Instead it consumed him in agonizing fire, and he died as planned in Nessus' revenge.

15. CLYTEMNESTRA and AEGISTHUS: Agamemnon, the leader of the Greek forces at the siege of Troy, was betrayed during his absence from Mycenae by the strong-willed Clytemnestra and her pliable paramour Aegisthus. Nursing a grudge against Agamemnon, Clytemnestra plotted with Aegisthus and they both murdered him at the banquet celebrating his homecoming.

16. LUCRETIA and SEXTUS: Sextus Tarquinius, the weak son of Lucius Tarquinius, the last Etruscan king of Rome, became inflamed by the beauty of the chaste Lucretia, wife of his fellow officer, Collatine. Secretly withdrawing from his camp at besieged Ardea, he returned to Rome and asked hospitality of Lucretia, which according to his estate was granted him. That night he violently ravished her, and in the morning returned to camp, without his absence being noticed. Lucretia in her grief dispatched messages to her father and husband, who came at once to her. Revealing her shame and the name of her violator she demanded revenge of them, and then stabbing herself in the breast she died. Vowing to root out the whole hated family of the Tarquins, they bore the bleeding body of Lucretia through the streets of Rome, and made the entire vile deed acquainted to the people. So moved were they that they rose against the Tarquins and drove them from Rome into perpetual exile. And so begins the Republic of Rome.

17. BYBLIS: Byblis was the daughter of Miletus and the twin sister of Kaunus, for whom she felt a lewd and guilty passion. The story of Byblis is a caution that a girl should love not unlawfully. Although warned never to confess her love to her brother, she does so by letter, which predictably horrifies Kaunus. He repulses her and takes off for places elsewhere. Becoming crazed, Byblis runs shrieking her love through the land in pursuit of her fleeing brother and eventually falls in exhaustion and, consumed by her own tears, she is changed into a fountain.

18. HERO and LEANDER: Leander, a youth of Abydos on the one side of the Hellespont, loved Hero, a priestess of Venus, in the town of Sestos situated on the other side. Each night he would swim the treacherous strait to enjoy the delights of her company. One night in a terrible tempest, not willing to forgo the favors of Hero, he unwisely attempted the waters. His strength overcome, he drowned, and his body carried by the currents was deposited on the European side beneath the tower of Hero. Made thus aware of his death, in despair Hero cast herself from her tower and perished in the same sea that had taken her lover.

19. PASIPHAË: Pasiphaë was the wife of King Minos of Crete. She conceived a strange and terrible passion for a beautiful bull that she gratified by means of an improbable subterfuge. The wooden frame of a cow was made for her by Daedalus, and she concealed herself therein. The rampant bull deceived by this device, mounting it, thereby effected a union with Pasiphaë resulting in the Minotaur.

20. OVID: Publius Ovidius Naso was born at Sulmo in the Pelignian country in 43 B.C. He was a Roman poet of great fame. His chief works were *Metamorphoses* and *Fasti*, but he was most admired by the populace for his love poems. His every verse immediately became the popular lyric of the moment. Sudden calamity and disgrace fell upon him in A.D. 8. Banished to the remote provinces of the Euxine Sea (the official reason given by Augustus being the immorality of his poetry), he spent the remainder of his days away from his beloved Rome and died in A.D. 18. It was from *Metamorphoses* that Boccaccio derived so much of his material on Greek mythology.

21. HECATE and CERES: Hecate was the sister of Latona. She also was the goddess of Enchantment. Ceres was the sister of Jupiter, to whom she bore Persephone who was later stolen away by Pluto. Ceres was the goddess of Agriculture, and when her daughter was provisionally restored to her by Pluto, who allowed her to return to her mother six months of the year, the renewal of Spring and the fecundity of Summer was created.

22. PAULUS AEMILIUS: A Roman general and patrician, he was Consul in 168 B.C. and ended the Third Macedonian War at Pydna. The captive king Perses of Macedonia was one of the trophies displayed at Paulus' triumphal return. Of the vast sums brought by him into the Roman treasury from his campaigns in Spain and Macedonia he kept nothing, preferring honor above all treasure.

23. MARCUS CURTIUS, ATTILIUS REGULUS, and VALERIUS PUBLICOLA: Of these three, the greatest example of public and civic virtue is perhaps Marcus Curtius, who lived in the fourth century B.C. According to legend, a chasm was formed in the Forum by an earthquake. The oracles announced that it could be closed only by the sacrifice of Rome's greatest treasure. The people were at a loss to interpret this when Marcus Curtius stepped forward and, declaring that the state possessed no greater treasure than a brave citizen in arms, he leaped, mounted and fully armored, into the chasm, which then closed after him. Attilius Regulus, according to Roman tradition, was sent by the Carthaginians to Rome in 250 B.C. to ask for peace or an exchange of prisoners. Having given his word as a prisoner of the Carthaginians to return to Carthage, when his mission produced no results—for the very good reason that he advised against either—he went back to Africa and was cruelly tortured to death. The third example of the virtuous life is Valerius Publicola of the opening years of the Roman Republic. Fiammetta would be hard put to back up this reference, for history records no special sacrifice attributed to him other than that he was four times elected Consul and was a liberal-minded public servant—no particular achievement, as Roman achievements go.

24. PHAEDRA and HIPPOLYTUS: Daughter of Pasiphaë and King Minos, Phaedra was the wife of the Athenian king Theseus. She fell hopelessly in love with her young stepson Hippolytus, and being repulsed by him in her lewd advances she falsely accused him to his father, thereby bringing on, through the easy credence of Theseus, his dramatic destruction and final metamorphoses.

25. ALCYDES: Another name for Hercules.

26. SEMIRAMIS and CLEOPATRA: Semiramis was an Assyrian princess and is the reputed founder of Babylon, a city renowned mainly for its licentious ways. Cleopatra was the Egyptian queen whose voluptuous enslavement of Marc Antony was the eventual cause of both their deaths. These women in their own time were said to be unprincipled in the satisfactions of their sexual appetites.

27. The children of LATONA: Driven homeless by the wrath of Juno, who jealously resented Latona's entanglement with Jupiter, pregnant Latona, in her search for a resting place, was finally accepted by the floating island of Delos. And here it was in a cave that the twins Apollo and Diana were born to the fugitive. Apollo was of course the god of the Sun, and Diana his sister, the huntress-goddess of the Moon.

28. TANAQUIL and SERVIUS TULLIUS: In legend, Servius Tullius was born of a slave in the household of Tarquinius Priscus. Tarquin's wife Tanaquil, who was prophetic, looking down on the sleeping child professed to see in him the future greatness of Rome. And so from that time forward she paid close attention to the supervision and development of the boy and man. She arranged his marriage to her own daughter by Tarquin, thereby guaranteeing the reality of her prophecy regarding his future. He eventually arrived at this by becoming the sixth king of Rome on the death of Tarquinius Priscus. He was later murdered by his own daughter and her husband Lucius Tarquinius, the father of Sextus, whose dreadful activity is recorded in the story of Lucretia.

29. POLYXENA and ACHILLES: During a truce between the Trojans and the Greeks, Achilles had seen and become captivated by Polyxena, the daughter of his enemy Priam. He agreed to use his influence with the Greeks to grant peace to Troy if Polyxena would be given him in marriage. While in the Temple of Apollo negotiating the marriage contract, Achilles was killed by Paris, the brother of Polyxena, shot through his vulnerable heel by a poisoned arrow. Achilles' spirit, speaking from beyond the grave, asked that Polyxena be now sacrificed so that his tomb lack not its fitting honor. And so, to appease the shade, she is offered up by the Greeks, to her own and the ghost of Achilles' satisfaction.

30. PERSEUS and ANDROMEDA: Perseus was the son of Jupiter and Danaë. Aided by the wingèd sandals loaned to him by Mercury, he spent his time flying about in search of adventure. Once, over Ethiopia, he chanced to look down, and from his aerial height saw Andromeda helplessly chained to a rock. Cepheus, her father, because of the overbearing pride of his wife Cassiopeia, had been commanded by the deities in punishment to expose his daughter thus, and to allow her to be devoured by the local monster of the region. It was at this crucial moment that Perseus entered the scene. The battle between Perseus and the monster was mighty, but Perseus prevailed and the virgin Andromeda was saved. Subsequent tests of valor and endurance followed, and victorious in each challenge, Perseus won the hand of Andromeda. Either Boccaccio or H.G. has Galeone in the *Seventh Question* substitute the name of Andromache for that of Andromeda, but this is so obvious an error it is corrected herein.

31. ORPHEUS and EURYDICE: Orpheus, the mythical musician whose voice and lyre had such a tranquillizing effect on all that heard him, loses his young wife to death. Inconsolable, he pleads in song with Persephone and her lord Pluto that Eurydice be restored to him. Melted by the sweet music, Pluto agrees, but does so with conditions. These conditions are broken by Orpheus on the return journey from Hades, and he loses Eurydice a second and final time.

32. MARS, VULCAN, and VENUS: Venus was the goddess of love and the wife of Vulcan, with whom she found little scope for the exercise of her particular talent. She is involved in an amour with Mars, and her indiscretion is disclosed to her husband by Phoebus, who evidently disapproved in fact as well as in principle. Vulcan was the god of fire as well as a blacksmith of some invention. He skillfully fashioned a net of bronze, so fine it escaped the detection of either Venus or Mars on whose unlawful couch he had placed it. In the midst of one of their many lovemakings they were caught and held fast in each other's arms. This disgraceful episode amused the gods greatly, and the discomfiture of Venus was the talk of Olympus.

33. The women of OMPHALE: When in a fit of madness, Hercules killed his friend Iphitus, he was condemned for this offense to become the slave of Queen Omphale for three years. During this service, Hercules' nature and behavior took on strange characteristics. He, who had formerly been a man among men, now lived effeminately, spending his days with the handmaidens of Omphale spinning wool and gossiping; and at times he even took to wearing the garments of women while Omphale charged around wearing his lion's skin, trophy of his first labor, the killing of the Nemaean lion. However, damage to his psyche was not permanent, for when his servitude was completed, he married Deianira and settled down in domestic bliss with her for three years. For reasons of his own, which may have been simple error, Boccaccio transposes this particular adventure of Hercules, and has it happen during his supposed infatuation with Iole many years later. This bit of carelessness weakens considerably the argument of Fiammetta.

34. CASSANDRA: Cassandra, another offspring of Troy's Priam, on her birth was gifted with prophecy by Apollo. She evidently was a bore, as so often are the portentous, for no one, least of all Paris, her brother, listened to her dreadful predictions. Had they done so, it is still hard to believe that the results would have been any different, the strategy, such as it was, being in the hands of the quarrelsome gods anyway.

35. SCYLLA: Scylla was the daughter of Nisus of Megara, an impregnable city under siege by Minos of Crete. Seeing Minos from the ramparts of Megara, Scylla fell in love with him, and in the hopes of furthering an exchange of love she cut from her father's brow the purple lock on which his safety depended. In spite of this dreadful act of betrayal, Minos scorned her. Because he would have none of her, Scylla, in a violent rage, leaped into the waters in pursuit of the Cretan ship carrying him back to Knossos. At this point the spirit of her dead father took a hand in the proceedings, and effected her transformation into a feathered bird. A strange and inconclusive act.

36. ARIADNE, THESEUS, and PHAEDRA: As a young man, Theseus, the son of Aegeus, joined a band of young people who were to be sent as sacrifice to the Minotaur in Crete; an annual tribute demanded by Minos. With the aid of Minos' daughter

Ariadne, Theseus slew the Minotaur and escaped, fleeing Crete in company with Ariadne. On his return journey to Athens he abandoned her on the island of Naxos. He never returned for her and years later married her younger sister Phaedra.

37. TEREUS, PROCNE, and PHILOMELA: For his aid in helping lift the siege of Athens, Tereus, king of Thrace, received in marriage Procne, the daughter of Pandion the king. Several years later, settled in Thrace with an infant son and her husband, Procne, still homesick for her family, prevailed upon Tereus to bring her sister Philomela from Athens for a visit. On the return journey Tereus in great lust ravished Philomela and then to cover his crime compounded it by cutting out her tongue and leaving her incarcerated in a well-guarded house hidden in a deep woods near the road to Thrace. Philomela embroidered the whole bloody story into a scarf and with the help of a sympathetic guard had it conveyed to her sister. With a sense of great outrage the two sisters took vengeance by killing Procne's infant son by Tereus and had him served as a special gourmet dish to his unwitting father.

38. PISISTRATUS: A favorite classical reference, particularly during the Renaissance, Pisistratus was historically credited with more villainy than the actual facts support. Following the benevolent rule of Solon, he entered Athenian history by seizing power in 560 B.C. and becoming Tyrant of Athens. Although twice driven out by an exasperated people, he persisted and, establishing himself firmly by 546, ruled until his death in 527. Francis Bacon, appointed Counsel for the Prosecution at the treason trial of his benefactor the Earl of Essex, in his closing argument dramatically stated that Essex was "not much unlike Pisistratus, of whom it was so anciently written how he gashed and wounded himself, and in that sort ran crying into Athens that his life was sought and like to have been taken away; thinking to have moved the people to have pitied him and taken his part by such counterfeited harm and danger: whereas his aim and drift was to take the government of the city into his hands, and alter the form thereof." Bacon's point was made, Essex was adjudged guilty and three days later met death by execution. Fiammetta's allusion to the cruelty of Pisistratus, which more properly should have been applied instead to the Tyrant's wife, refers, incorrectly, to certain lines in Canto 15, Purgatory, of the *Divine Comedy*, in which the lady demands of her husband that he inflict the punishment of death upon a presumptuous youth who, so inflamed with love for their daughter, did publicly snatch a kiss from the girl in the marketplace. Actually, Pisistratus turned aside this cruel request with the soft answer:

> How shall we those requite
> Who wish us evil, if we thus condemn
> The man that loves us?

Fiammetta and her circle would be presumed to have been well acquainted with Dante's masterpiece at the time Boccaccio was writing the *Filocolo*, and the meetings in the cloister of Sant' Arcangelo à Baiano most certainly would have included many discussions of the *Divine Comedy*. Fiammetta's misattribution of cruelty to Pisistratus is not therefore easily explained.

39. LAODAMIA and PROTESILAUS: The Oracle had declared that victory in the Trojan War should be the lot of that party from which should fall the first victim. Seeking that honor, Protesilaus was the first to leap from the ship of the invading Greeks and engage in combat on the beaches of Troy. His opponent was Hector, and the prophecy was indeed fulfilled. Laodamia, on the news of her husband's death, refused to accept it and prevailed upon the gods to allow her one more conversation with him. She was given three hours, and Protesilaus was returned by Mercury, conductor of the dead as well as messenger of the gods, to the upper world for a final reunion with Laodamia. He then dies a second time, and in grief she dies with him.

40. DIONYSIUS, the tyrant of Syracuse: Bored to distraction by the constant praises of Damocles who flattered and chattered incessantly on the happiness of kings, Dionysius rebuked him by seating him at a royal banquet directly beneath a sword suspended by a single hair. By this sardonic use of poetic realism, Dionysius conveyed to the sycophantic Damocles the precariousness of power.

A NOTE

about the typeface used in this book

Around 1675 Anton Janson, punchcutter and typefounder of Leipsic, Germany, issued a type specimen sheet presenting for the first time the original of the charming booktype which now bears his name. Although since that time punchcutters have greatly altered the fine old classic face in recutting and refining it, neither the sharpness nor the beautiful clarity of the original has been lost.

Until fairly recently, definite and accurate information concerning Janson was obscure. However, it is now known that he was born in 1620 in Wauden, Vriesland, that he served his apprenticeship in Amsterdam, and that he settled in Leipsic in 1656. Attracted to this university center by his hope for greater appreciation of his talents, he was not disappointed. By the time he died, in 1687, he was well known and respected.

Ownership of his matrices fell to various houses both in Leipsic and in Frankfort until eventually they came into possession of the printer Drugulin. In 1868 pseudo-Janson type specimen sheets were published by this house and given the name *Renaissance-Hollandisch*, which became known popularly as the *Old Dutch Face*. Janson's obscurity was complete. In 1919 the matrices were sold by Drugulin to Stempel of Frankfort, who erroneously renamed them *Janson*. Since then they have been further refined for machine and phototypography, and their resemblance to the original is now vestiginal. What does remain, however, is the clear and precise classicism of Janson's early Dutch training.

Designed by Harry Carter
Composed on the Videocomp at Haddon Craftsmen
in 12 point Janson
Printed by Halliday Lithograph Corporation
On Warren Old Style Wove Offset
Bound by Halliday Lithograph Corporation
in Devon Cloth